GREEN ENERGY

GREEN ENERGY

How to Build a Sustainable Future

Nicole Kobie

Cornerstone Press

1 3 5 7 9 10 8 6 4 2

Cornerstone Press
20 Vauxhall Bridge Road
London SW1V 2SA

Cornerstone Press is part of the Penguin Random House
group of companies whose addresses can be found at
global.penguinrandomhouse.com

First published in the UK by Cornerstone Press in 2022

www.penguin.co.uk

A CIP catalogue record for this book is available from the British
Library.

ISBN 9781847943293

Typeset in 9.5/18 pt Exchange Text
by Integra Software Services Pvt. Ltd, Pondicherry

Printed and bound in Great Britain by Clays Ltd, Elcograf S.p.A.

The authorised representative in the EEA is Penguin Random House
Ireland, Morrison Chambers, 32 Nassau Street, Dublin D02 YH68.

Penguin Random House is committed to a sustainable future for
our business, our readers and our planet. This book is made from
Forest Stewardship Council® certified paper.

Contents

CONTENTS

Introduction

In Australia, 2020 began in horror as wildfires sparked by heat and drought blazed across 186,000 square kilometres in Queensland, killing thirty-four people and more than a billion animals. The next year was no better: floods swept across Europe, drowning towns; unprecedented winter weather was seen in Madrid, Spain and Texas, USA; the Philippines recorded the strongest typhoon ever seen in spring; Siberia reported a heatwave; a heat dome in the west of North America caused record high temperatures, sparking a fire that engulfed the entire community of Lytton, Canada. And in Japan, Kyoto's cherry blossoms bloomed a month earlier than expected. If such messages weren't strong enough, the UN's climate change report by the Intergovernmental Panel on Climate Change (IPCC) said the unprecedented impacts of anthropogenic global warming could already be irreversible. So, what can be done?

Three-quarters[1] of global greenhouse gases come from energy alone – that includes producing electricity, fuelling cars and other transport, powering industry and heating homes. That means that, for our own future, the future of energy must be clean and free from carbon and other damaging emissions. The world's shift to renewables has been too slow, but progress is being made. Coal is slowly fading from use, with even China refusing to fund coal-burning plants in other countries, while natural gas is next to go, as high prices and risk of stranded assets, such as pipeline infrastructure that may soon be obsolete, make it less and less appealing even to fossil-fuel incumbents. Owing to mass production, the price of solar panels has more than halved, while, as offshore turbines grow in size to epic dimensions, wind has now become the cheapest way to make electricity. Biomass, such as the burning of wood, is fuelling old coal plants, recycled cooking oil is powering planes, and green hydrogen could soon clean up transport and industry. But there is still a long way to go and not a great deal of time in which to make the necessary adjustments.

Perversely, the effects of climate change are stymying our ability to generate energy. Consider oil: the increasingly intense hurricanes hitting the Gulf of Mexico knocked 80 per cent of oil production offline in 2021, while freezing weather in Texas, exacerbated by climate change,[2] led to deadly household blackouts. Hydropower plants in Malawi and California have been unable to generate following droughts – or they have been wiped out entirely by floods in China and India. These instances show that, now more than ever, we need a greater variety of reliable energy sources to tap into.

Climate change is the existential elephant in the room, but there are other ways by which our existing energy production is killing us. Air pollution kills ten million people a year, causes asthma and other breathing disorders in children, and worsened the health effects of Covid-19. Cars and trucks need to shift away from internal combustion engines to electric motors in order to limit carbon emissions, and also to improve air quality in our growing cities. But electric vehicles are the beginning, not the end. We know that industry pumping filth into our air is bad for public health, but cooking and heating through burning wood at home is an equally serious problem that hurts hardest the most vulnerable in developing countries. Because of our reliance on fossil fuels for energy, the air at work, outside and in our homes is killing us.

If that wasn't enough, another financial cost to oil and gas that is often hidden behind newspaper headlines is the security turmoil caused by access to precious fossil fuels. Such conflict should be impossible to ignore, yet we accept this additional expense unthinkingly when we're at the pumps to refill cars or are paying energy bills. Others don't have it so lucky: Ukraine's gas supply has been shut off by Russia as part of diplomatic disputes multiple times, and such fossil-fuel diplomacy – or lack of it – could be one reason why the UK and EU faced gas shortages and subsequent high prices over the winter of 2021–22.

Overhauling our energy production methods has the potential to empower us to take control and counter such challenges, but transitioning to clean energy is more than just a way to avert the worst impacts of climate change, pollution or politics. It's also an opportunity to build a better world, bringing light and heat to impoverished people through microgrids as well as empowering the global south to sell excess clean energy to wealthier countries through linked-up grids.

The future of energy isn't something to fear or to try to hold back. It's marvellously exciting – not only because it is healthier, safer and cheaper, but because there are remarkable feats of engineering coming our way. And it's beautiful, too, with cleaner air, quieter transport and safer energy. Imagine 250-metre-tall turbines harnessing ocean winds, or solar panels capturing the sun in the desert, on Italian rooftops and English pavements. Or underwater turbines pulling power from rivers, canals, waves and tides, or power stored in hilltops for whenever it is needed.

We need this change, but it's happening too slowly. Over the past thirty years, despite the desperate push to ditch coal and electrify everything, the proportion of energy produced from renewable sources has barely changed. In this book, I'll explore the complex technical, engineering and financial reasons for energy inertia. Shifting to new production technologies requires innovative thinking from industry incumbents, government policy makers and new players such as startups – not only with energy generation but sharing it through grids, storing it in batteries and using it via electrical infrastructure. That's further delayed by incumbent fossil-fuel companies digging in their heels to slow the process, hoping to make the most from their investments before these changes threaten their business models.

The future of energy is renewable – it has to be. Now we just need to make it happen.

1

The slow death of coal – and the even slower rise of renewables

---

The twelve cooling towers of Drax Power Station loom over the village of Drax, near Selby, North Yorkshire, a bleak backdrop to small streets of brick homes and farmers' fields. Within ten years of starting operation in the 1970s, it was the largest power plant in the UK, generating electricity for six million British homes, all by burning coal. By 2012, it provided 7 per cent of the UK's electricity, by itself. All the while, the chimney at Drax – the tallest in Britain – churned out smoke, giving that stack the single largest carbon footprint of any structure in the country.[1]

That made the plant the target of climate change activists. Several hundred protesters attempted but failed to invade the plant in a 2006 campaign dubbed the 'Battle of Drax'. Despite the military language and thirty-eight arrests, newspaper reports[2] suggest the demonstration atmosphere was more a festival than an invasion. Two years later, Camp for Climate Action campaigners wearing high-viz jackets and hard hats impersonated Network Rail staff and halted a train carrying coal to the plant. Over sixteen hours, the forty activists shovelled 20 tonnes of coal onto the tracks under a banner demanding 'leave it in the ground'; though the train driver remarked the campaigners were 'polite and friendly', twenty-nine people were arrested.[3] Coal continued to be burned, smoke still billowed from the chimney.

What a difference a few years makes. Drax began to move away from coal in 2012, shifting four of its six systems to burning wood pellets, known as biomass. The UK government soon afterwards announced it was phasing out coal altogether by 2025, though the deadline has since been brought forward by a year.[4] In 2017, the UK had its first coal-free day. Just three years later, the country reported its longest stretch of electricity production without any coal since the Industrial Revolution, totting up 67 days, 22 hours and 55 minutes – ironically, it was cut short because Drax needed to fire up a coal unit for maintenance. Two of Drax's generation systems are still set up to burn coal, but in 2021 they were removed from regular production and placed on standby as backup. They were used later that year amid a gas shortage that saw electricity prices skyrocket in the early autumn.[5]

The trajectory of Drax Power Station has been reflected across the country. Coal powered the Industrial Revolution, supplying 95 per cent of electricity demand by 1913, with that dominance continuing throughout the next century; by 1970, it still made up half of energy production. Following the government's edict – and the slow awakening to climate change – coal use collapsed by 2019, making up just 1.8 per cent of the UK's energy supply.

That such a shift has happened in the UK feels miraculous. Soon coal will be dead in the UK, a country that burned so much of the stuff that its capital city was once infamous for smog. And the trend is being echoed across Europe, with twelve countries no longer using coal, including Albania, Austria and Sweden.[6] In 2020, coal use in the US fell to its lowest levels since 1965,[7] while projects to build coal plants have been cancelled across South America.[8] Now we need to make that happen across the rest of the world: in Australia, it still makes up 80 per cent of the country's electricity generation,[9] while India, China and the rest of Southeast Asia burn three-quarters of the coal used in the world.

Progress is slower than you think

Drax shows that fossil fuels such as coal are dying – but hold the celebrations for now; it's a slow, painful, protracted death. Despite the swift progress of the last few years, there's more to the story, even in a country like the UK that is actively killing off coal. Indeed, as of 2019, despite all but ditching coal, fossil fuels still made up 79 per cent of the UK's energy mix.

Wait, you might be thinking, *that doesn't sound right*? After all, according to UK government figures for 2020, renewable sources topped fossil fuels for electricity production for the very first time, at 43 per cent versus 39 per cent. That's an accomplishment worth popping the cork on a bottle of carbonated bubbles. But those figures conceal dirty truths.

Here are three to start:

1) Electricity generation isn't the only source of fossil-fuel emissions;
2) Coal isn't being replaced by renewable sources;
3) Percentages obfuscate actual production, as they conceal the total amount of fossil fuels being used as energy *consumption* increases.

Let's start with the first factor. There's a key distinction to be made between two terms: *energy* mix and *electricity* mix. They are not interchangeable. Electricity makes up only one aspect of the energy used by a country, alongside fuel for transport and heating for homes, and those latter two slices remain largely dependent on fossil fuels, even in a forward-looking country like the UK. Petrol and diesel continue to dominate transport in the UK and most other countries, while natural gas remains the main source of energy for home heating.

Renewables top the fossil fuels for *electricity* production in the UK, but the overall *energy* mix is only 20 per cent from low-carbon sources (that's renewable and nuclear) with the remaining 80 per cent from fossil fuels. That's thanks to the continued reliance on petrol and diesel for cars and lorries, and gas for home heating, a pattern that's echoed across the world. Globally, *electricity* is slowly shifting to renewables, with a third of the world's *electricity* mix already 'low carbon', which is that mix of nuclear and other renewables, such as hydro and solar.[10] However, the global *energy* mix is half as clean, with only 16 per cent from 'low-carbon' sources. In order to genuinely clean up our energy, we need renewable sources for not just electricity production but off-grid energy such as fuels as well.

That's the first problem. The second is that any celebration of the death of coal is marred by what the UK and other countries are using in its place. While the UK has dramatically ditched that particular fossil fuel, coal has for the most part been replaced by natural gas for electricity production. In 1990, coal made up two-thirds of electricity production in the UK, with gas at just 1.6 per cent. Thirty years on, that has flipped, with coal at just 1.7 per cent and natural gas now the dominant single production material, at 37 per cent. That pattern of shifting from coal to gas has been repeated in many places around the world, including the US, though the EU has had more success replacing coal with renewable sources.

There is some good news here. At least half of the UK's production gap from ditching coal has been made up with low-carbon alternatives other than gas, led by wind power at 24 per cent and nuclear at 17 per cent. Second, gas *is* better than coal in terms of emissions and how it works alongside intermittent renewable sources, such as wind and solar. 'Coal is one of the most carbon-intensive fuels – when it's burned it releases the most CO_2 ... so that's what we should phase out first,' says Christine Shearer, programme director for coal at analyst firm Global Energy Monitor (GEM), which tracks the death of coal alongside the rise of renewable energy.

That's one reason why swapping out coal in favour of gas is an idea that's been encouraged by the fossil-fuel industry, which has spent billions of dollars lobbying governments to convince them of the merit of natural gas. Indeed, even the term 'natural gas' shows the power of branding and marketing, with the 'natural' moniker for a gas that's predominantly methane obscuring its full climate impact.[11] 'I think the oil and gas industry has done a good job of portraying natural gas as a clean bridge fuel towards renewables,' Shearer adds.

Beyond carbon emissions, coal doesn't work as well as gas alongside renewable sources, some of which can be intermittent with supply – when it's not windy or the sun isn't shining, power plants can't produce electricity – meaning alternative sources need to be powered up to fill the gap. Because natural gas can be cycled up and down – how the industry says, 'turned off and on' – more easily than coal in power plants, it fits better alongside renewable sources. However, that's also true of hydro and biomass, which don't have as much of a climate impact as natural gas.

So, first we have to realise we have an energy challenge bigger than electricity; and second, much of what has replaced coal to date has been so-called natural gas, which is another polluting fossil fuel. That leads us to the third problem: energy use is growing. And as the overall pie gets bigger, so too do the slices.

Though electricity is undoubtedly becoming cleaner, with a higher proportion of it generated from renewable and fossil-free sources, such as nuclear, we still need to consider the total amount of energy we use. More people around the world are using more electricity. In many ways this is good news, as it can be a positive sign of development and people exiting poverty, and also reflects the shift to electric vehicles and heating. 'We think about climate action in terms of just substituting our existing fossil-fuel generation for renewable, as a one-to-one swap and then we're done,' says Seaver Wang, climate and energy analyst at the Breakthrough Institute. 'This doesn't account for the fact that global energy demand is going to increase at a dramatic rate, which is good for standards of living, but we expect something like a doubling of global electricity usage over the next thirty years.'

In developed nations, energy consumption over the last few decades has been largely flat, but globally the amount of energy consumed has tripled since 1965. This means that even if the proportion of coal, gas and oil in the mix is falling, the actual raw amount being burned is still climbing. Measured by consumption, the energy produced by coal alone has tripled globally in that same time period, despite efforts to reduce its use.

This in turn means that we don't just need wind, solar and hydro to meet current use, but future demand, too. We simply need more electricity. After all, pollution-preventing innovations such as electric cars are only free from operational emissions if they're powered by clean electricity. Otherwise, we're simply shifting where the pollution happens, which has benefits but doesn't address the existential challenge of the climate crisis. That's why percentages or proportions of an energy mix matter less than the raw numbers, and there's nowhere that challenge is more obvious than China.

China and coal

China is a renewables giant, leading the world in the production of solar and wind energy. However, it also uses the most coal. Though the country is the largest solar generator on the planet, solar makes up just 3 per cent of China's electricity mix. 'The fundamental contradiction of China is that it's both the number one site of coal plants and also the number one site of renewable power,' Shearer says. That's because China's 1.4 billion citizens are ramping up their use of electricity, increasing it by an order of magnitude over the past fifty or so years; in 1965, total energy consumption was 1,532TWh (terawatt-hours)[12] versus 39,361TWh in 2019.[13] And it could well go much higher – per capita, Chinese people still use half as much energy annually as the average American.

So while the proportion of coal in China's energy mix has fallen from 87 per cent in 1965 to 58 per cent in 2019, its total coal use has increased sixteen-fold.[14] In other words, the good news is that China has slashed the proportion of coal in its energy mix, but the bad news is that the country is burning more coal than ever. As the UK and Europe raced to shut their coal plants, 96 per cent of the new coal plants announced in the first half of 2021 were being built in China, according to Global Energy Monitor.

Just as China's domestic coal situation is confusing, its international position has also proved ambiguous and subject to change. Beyond its own domestic coal-burning plants, China has remained one of the last funders for projects in other countries, in particular in Asia and Africa, pledging $160 billion to support overseas coal plants in the six years to 2020. While half of those were cancelled due to financial and political instability, it has long seemed likely that China would be the country that builds the last coal plant, or at the very least finances it.

But then President Xi Jinping surprised a UN General Assembly meeting in 2021 when he announced that China would stop financing overseas coal plants to help meet China's goal of peak carbon emissions by 2030 and full carbon neutrality by 2060. 'China will step up support for other developing countries in developing green and low-carbon energy, and will not build new coal-fired power projects abroad,' he said, though it's worth noting he did not pledge to do the same inside the country, with twenty-four new domestic projects announced in the first half of 2021 alone.

China was the last public financier of coal projects, after Japan and South Korea stopped funding overseas plants earlier in the year, says Leo Roberts, research manager at think tank E3G. 'China was the last refuge of the scoundrel,' he says. 'If you wanted a new coal project financed, China was where you went for your money.' China didn't necessarily pay for the entirety of the project, but its funding would underpin coal projects, helping to draw additional finance. 'China is involved in over 40GW worth of projects around the world across twenty countries,' he says. 'And now, suddenly, without China, all those projects are looking really shaky.' Roberts says more than half of African coal projects and 40 per cent of those in Asia could be ditched because of the pledge.

Of course, China is still building coal projects locally, though Roberts hopes that a shift away from domestic coal projects is looming, too, as the economics no longer make sense. As it's an old technology, there are few ways to squeeze down coal prices through innovation alone. Instead, coal prices tend to be influenced by supply and demand, with shortages leading to price spikes. In 2021, amid record high prices for coal, the Chinese government had to tell local producers to increase supply to help drive down the costs of generating energy.[15] Solar panels, on the other hand, have become cheaper to mass produce, easier to install and more efficient at generating electricity, meaning even a new solar farm will cost less than an existing coal plant.[16] This is also true for wind farms.

A report from Carbon Tracker shows that in China existing coal plants cost more to run than installing and operating a new wind or solar project.[17] But the financials of coal projects don't make sense even in places where the wider economy is dependent on coal. 'India has huge coal reserves, lots of people working in coal mines, and the Indian railways employ over a million people, and that relies hugely on transporting coal around for its income,'

Roberts adds. 'But even there, the economics are so bad that if you build a new coal power station, it will become a stranded asset in the very new future [as renewable prices fall].'

But even as the cost of coal makes it less and less attractive as an energy source, and even without new plants being financed by China, many industrialised countries still have existing plants burning the dirty stuff for power. That's why UN Secretary-General António Guterres targeted coal at the launch of the most recent report from the IPCC, which warned that climate change was 'unprecedented' and may be 'irreversible'. Guterres called for no new coal plants to be built after 2021, but he didn't stop there. 'OECD countries must phase out existing coal by 2030, with all others following suit by 2040,' he said.[18] 'Countries should also end all new fossil fuel exploration and production, and shift fossil fuel subsidies into renewable energy.' For that to happen, Guterres noted, solar and wind capacity needs to quadruple. But will it?

Slow shift to renewables

Coal is slow to die. But why are renewables failing to pick up the slack? Despite the existential threat of the climate crisis, little has changed in electricity production. As of 2020, 61 per cent of global electricity production comes from coal, gas and oil, with a further 10 per cent from nuclear power.[19] Half of what remains is from hydro, at 16 per cent of the total. Those global figures haven't changed significantly in the last thirty-five years.

That's in part because renewable sources come with their own set of challenges. Using water, sun and wind for power are ancient ideas, but doing so at scale for the modern world requires developing, testing and installing new technologies. Hydroelectric is well understood and heavily used, but we're still figuring out the best way to build wind and solar farms that are efficient and financially viable. Investment can be difficult, and therefore these projects require government support; hauling oil or coal out of the ground is also costly, but we know it works, so it's easier to finance.

Another challenge is intermittent supply. With fossil-fuel systems you can simply burn more gas and coal to meet spikes in demand, and extra demand can also be met in similar ways with some renewable sources, such as hydro and biomass. But that doesn't work with wind or solar power if the wind isn't blowing or the sun isn't shining. Indeed, slower winds over the summer of 2021 contributed to rising energy prices amid low supply across Europe, sparking demand for more gas from Russia and causing the few remaining coal plants in the UK to be powered up, including at Drax.[20] Such intermittency is a solvable problem, but it means grids need updating, storage solutions have to be installed, and alternative sources must be in place – and that's expensive and time-consuming. 'It's a fundamental shift in how the power system was created and designed,' Shearer says.

Solving such problems is the domain of innovators, engineers and the investors and governments who fund them. Renewables naysayers point to the fact that there's no major country that's successfully ditched fossil fuels as evidence that it's not possible to do so. 'But it's also a lack of resources, lack of imagination, lack of political will and a lot of resistance from fossil-fuel interests,' Shearer adds.

Plenty of individual countries have overcome these challenges to make significant progress, especially with electricity. Albania and Portugal both have entirely renewable electricity production, thanks to hydroelectric dams, while half of Denmark's electricity comes from wind power alone. Iceland's electricity is almost entirely from hydro and geothermal, with the latter used for heating homes and water, meaning the country's overall energy mix is mostly carbon-free, too. Germany's main source of electricity is wind power, at a quarter of production, and its solar use is growing, too. Three-quarters of Honduras' electricity is renewable, with 12 per cent coming from solar, making it the world leader in terms of penetration rates. In the UK, the coal era that started in the Industrial Revolution is almost over, and a quarter of electricity now comes from wind, with 42 per cent from renewable sources. This progress is proof that change is possible.

Smaller countries may show the way, but the real impact comes from global superpowers following their lead. The successes of Iceland or Denmark can inspire and provide technology, but without progress in countries such as China, the US, India and Russia, the gains are limited. Larger countries are where the real progress for the whole planet will happen – and progress is being made, even if slowly and inconsistently.

What have those larger countries managed to accomplish? In the US, the use of coal by share of electricity consumption has halved since 1985. China's electricity mix remains about two-thirds coal-powered, but that is down from 80 per cent in 2007. Russia continues to depend on gas, but renewable sources are now a fifth of production. If any of those countries could follow the lead of Iceland or Denmark, it would make a real difference.

And it's worth noting that renewable energy brings with it benefits beyond avoiding the worst of the impacts from climate change. If record high temperatures, wildfires, droughts and floods aren't enough to convince that alternatives are worth the effort, don't forget that renewables can be cheaper and help countries secure their energy independence, meaning they're no longer at the whim of global oil, gas and coal prices – or neighbours stopping supply, as Russia has stood accused of doing to the EU and UK over the summer of 2021, contributing to an energy crisis in the UK. Look at Iceland: shifting away from coal and oil to geothermal has saved the tiny northern nation $8.2 billion since the 1990s, helping to turn the small nation from a poor European neighbour to one of the richest per capita in the world, all while dramatically reducing its carbon emissions. Not bad for thirty years of effort and investment.

The simple fact is this: the costs of coal, gas and oil are too high. If we fully understood back in the 1800s the environmental damage that would be wrought by coal, we wouldn't – hopefully, though perhaps that's wishful thinking – have used it to power the Industrial Revolution and everything that's come since. Now that we know better, it's time to invest in the alternatives – and our own future.

2

The big players: hydro, wind and solar

Engineered waterfalls cascading over concrete and steel. Huge 260-metre-tall turbines turning in the winds kilometres offshore. Sun-catching arrays stretching across the desert. Boreholes reaching deep into the earth to tap volcanoes. Paving stones that collect our steps, shipping containers that turn plate scrapings into power, buoys that capture the rise and fall of ocean waves. The technologies seeking to displace fossil fuels are nothing short of remarkable and ingenious, capturing the power inherent in our natural world. Of course, each of these methods has challenges that need to be acknowledged, and that includes the well-understood heavy hitters such as hydro, wind and solar, as well as wave and tidal, geothermal, biomass and niche ideas such as kinetic energy and waste reclamation. But more often than not, these criticisms also apply to fossil fuels, and developing these green energies still has vast potential to reinvent how we power our lives.

One of the main stumbling blocks is that many of these alternative generation techniques are only carbon-free *operationally*. That means a renewable-powered plant doesn't emit carbon when it's producing electricity, but the building of it certainly did. As we roll out new energy generation techniques we will inevitably accrue carbon costs, whether it's constructing a concrete dam, steel turbines or plastic-encased solar panels. This criticism is valid, but the same is true for building fossil-fuel power plants that will not produce carbon-free energy, meaning that even if these downsides are considered, renewables are still the better option.

Another point to consider is environmental impact beyond carbon emissions. Building a hydroelectric dam floods huge swathes of land, while wind turbine blades can have a negative impact, to put it mildly, on birds and bats.

Those criticisms are fair, but again, it's also true for fossil fuels that will contribute to operational pollution. Take a look at the damage wrought by the Canadian tar sands as an example, with toxic waste killing birds en masse and potentially poisoning local indigenous communities' water supplies – wind turbines undoubtedly cause less damage to animals than such fossil-fuel extraction projects.

And then there are the costs. As many renewable sources remain in early stages of technological development, that means higher prices for equipment and installation. Those costs will fall with time, as equipment becomes mass produced, supply chains solidify and technologies are perfected. Solar panels were once deemed too expensive to install on home roofs, but are now mass produced in China, with prices falling to negligible levels; in response, the price of solar power has fallen by 89 per cent over the past decade. Of course, infrastructure needs to be installed – be it cabling to connect mountainous wind farms to power grids or dams for hydro – but that was once true for petrol, gas and coal; we've just been using them for so long that much of those costs is now sunk and forgotten. Indeed, when a new pipeline needs to be installed, billions of dollars are offered by governments; in Canada, the multibillion-dollar Keystone XL pipeline to the US was scrapped, leaving the public purse $1.3 billion (CAN) out of pocket.[1] We're accustomed to accepting such costs for oil, but not renewables, despite the clear benefits of the latter.

The point isn't to ignore these challenges when it comes to renewables, but to understand that such hurdles were also faced by existing energy production techniques, alongside other serious downsides like greenhouse-gas emissions. While we should mitigate as many of the downsides of renewables as possible when making this global shift to new ways of generating power, let's not forget that what we're leaving behind is much worse – and that's before the impact of carbon is even considered. With that in mind, here's the future of the big three renewable sources of energy – hydro, wind and solar.

Hydroelectric

China's Three Gorges Dam spans 2.3 kilometres across the Yangtze River, with gargantuan walls of steel and concrete holding back a reservoir of water that stretches more than 1,000 square kilometres. The largest hydroelectric dam in the world, Three Gorges generates 22.5GW of electricity at its peak, though seasonal changes to water levels mean it can't always produce its maximum, so on average its output is closer to 14GW.

Though epic in size and engineering, dams work via simple principles. Cascading water is used to turn turbines, which generate electricity by moving electromagnets past a conductor. The largest hydroelectric plants, such as Three Gorges and the Itaipu Dam straddling the border between Brazil and Paraguay, use a dam to create a reservoir of water that can be sent hurtling past such equipment – though large rivers can also be used by diverting a section of the water through turbines.

Hydroelectric remains the most popular renewable source of energy across the world, powering 16 per cent of electricity globally, followed by wind (5.3 per cent) and then solar (2.7 per cent).[2] The modern version was put to use in the Industrial Revolution like coal, but its use took off in the 1930s, spurred by the American New Deal's flood of investment into infrastructure. While concerns about the impacts of dams and reservoirs sparked a decline in hydroelectric projects, the shift to renewables has renewed interest, with 65 per cent growth in hydropower capacity in the 2010s.[3] So why is hydroelectric so popular?

One reason why hydroelectricity is so well used around the world is that it's a proven, understood and reliable way to make energy. Another major advantage is that hydroelectric plants are responsive to demand – something that intermittent renewables like solar and wind aren't. Flip the switch and water starts pouring through immediately, meaning there's little delay to getting more energy; they're even faster than combustion turbines powered by gas.[4] Plus, water can be pumped back up into the dam at off-peak times in order to be prepared for high demand, letting reservoirs act as giant wet batteries. Effectively, you can have carbon-free energy on tap, which is a significant benefit.

There are, however, downsides to hydro, beginning with the high construction cost. Building Itaipu required $20 billion and precipitated a diplomatic dispute between Brazil and Paraguay. Such issues are common, with 90 per cent of projects exceeding their already considerable budgets since the 1930s.[5] There are also considerable environmental damages wrought in their construction, in particular with all the steel and concrete required to dam a river. The Three Gorges Dam used 16 million cubic metres of concrete, a material with an intense carbon footprint.

Flooding to create a reservoir also wipes out entire ecosystems and communities. Turkey sparked international outrage for the 2019 flooding of a 12,000-year-old town, Hasankeyf, in order to build a dam on the Tigris River,[6] while the creation of Three Gorges displaced 1.2 million people.[7] In Canada, the Muskrat Falls dam will not only flood a massive area of land, but risks poisoning land downstream, making it unhealthy for local Inuit groups to continue eating fish or hunting the animals that live off them.[8] This is because when large areas of land are flooded to make reservoirs for hydroelectric dams, microbes in the water turn mercury that is already latent in the soil into methylmercury, and this neurotoxin is absorbed by fish or other animals. Of twenty-two dams being considered by Canada, research suggests that 90 per cent of them could be impacted by this effect.

Once built, dams have other impacts. The vast reservoirs can be a source of methane, a greenhouse gas that is created when plant matter and other organic debris decay. And when hundreds of square kilometres of land are flooded, there's plenty of material rotting in the water giving off methane. While troubling, it's worth noting such emissions are much less than the methane produced at coal power stations, though.

Dams also face the consequences of climate change, beginning with the increasing scarcity of water.

Electricity generation makes up 16 per cent of water use by human activity, second only to food production.[9] But droughts sparked by climate change can cause blackouts, as has already been seen in recent years in California,[10] Venezuela,[11] Malawi[12] and Brazil.[13] When hydroelectric plants dry up, it's often during hot weather, just as residents in affected cities crank up the air conditioning. That means local power utilities respond by turning to alternative sources, including fossil fuels, worsening the cycle of climate change. In Syria, reduced water levels in the Euphrates River risks leaving locals without water for drinking or crops, as well as facing blackouts.[14] And in Brazil, along the Amazon River in particular, the felling of trees to build dams is likely what sparked the reduction in rain that caused lower water levels in the first place, highlighting the challenges of making hydroelectric power work when disruptive reservoirs are required.[15]

On the other hand, intense rain and ensuing floods sparked by climate change leave dams at risk of catastrophic failure. In 2021 alone, the Xinfa dam in Mongolia collapsed after built-in flood mitigations[16] proved insufficient against the unprecedented rainfall, while ice, water and debris from melting glaciers overwhelmed the Rishiganga dam in Uttarakhand, India, killing dozens of people.[17] Chinese authorities blew up a dam in 2020 to reduce fatal flooding on the Chuhe River,[18] and Three Gorges has had to make regular use of its floodgates to avoid damage.

Despite these challenges, dams continue to be built. Indeed, the idea is booming in the global south, despite serious political and economic issues. For example, the Grand Ethiopian Renaissance Dam on the Blue Nile will divert 13.5 billion cubic metres of water, raising concerns about water levels in downstream countries, including Sudan and Egypt, which use the river for power, agriculture and drinking water for millions. That could cause strife in an area already troubled with discord.

Choosing where to site a new hydroelectric dam is key to the future of these gargantuan building projects. In the future, they simply won't work where drought or floods are a risk, and are best deployed where water isn't in high demand for drinking or agriculture. 'You need water and topography,' notes Charles Rougé, lecturer in water resilience at the University of Sheffield. 'Historically, places where it's been successful are Canada, where in [the province of] British Columbia it's 90 per cent of electricity production, because you have lots of water and mountains, and not that many people.'

Despite these drawbacks, smaller projects and innovative startups are revealing solutions that could make the technology more effective and beneficial to the environment. For example, we don't necessarily need massive reservoirs held back by concrete dams to make carbon-free electricity using water. One idea long used on a smaller scale for microgeneration is diversion, also known as 'run of river'. This works especially where rivers have a notably steep gradient, with a section of water running through generators and the rest left to continue freely.

That idea is being extended for smaller installations around the world. In the US, Gravity Renewables builds small, distributed hydropower systems to install in rivers and canals. One system, in Seneca Falls, New York, makes use of a drop in elevation between canals to generate enough electricity to power 1,800 homes, while another in Pawtucket, Rhode Island, has repurposed a nineteenth-century mill to power 672 local homes.

German startup Smart Hydro Power has its own take on the idea, designing floating micro-hydroelectric plants that sit in the middle of rivers so the flowing water can turn the turbines to create enough electricity for local areas. One project, in a river near Akwanga, Nigeria, gives people in the small, remote village access to off-grid electricity, while a submerged turbine installed in Rosenheim, Germany, provides power locally, with any excess that is produced being fed into the local grid. Belgian startup Turbulent provides electricity for rural communities as well as industrial businesses looking for cleaner energy, by building small water-slide-style turbines alongside canals.

Such smaller projects suggest bigger may not be better when it comes to hydroelectric. They can't produce anywhere near the amount of power of an epic dam, but they come without many of the challenges. Plus, as the Nigerian example from Smart Hydro Power shows, micro-hydro can offer power to rural communities unconnected to national grids that currently overrely on fossil fuels such as coal or wood for heating and cooking. It also offers companies ways to generate their own energy. Massive hydroelectric dams and reservoirs will continue to be built in the future, but they'll be joined by smaller turbines tucked away in canals and rivers, adding clean power to the mix without the environmental damage or building costs of their bigger siblings.

Wind

Head to Britain's rugged Yorkshire coastline, and then carry on 130 kilometres into the North Sea. Halfway to

Denmark is Dogger Bank. Set in shallow waters, this 17,600-square-kilometre sandbank was once part of land that connected the UK to the continent – and thanks to a wind farm currently in construction, it will soon allow the UK, Denmark, Germany and the Netherlands to be linked up with renewable power.

The project has been in the works since 2008, when Dogger Bank was identified as an ideal location to site a wind farm. First, it's offshore, negating any complaints from locals and also ensuring consistent winds. Thanks to those relatively shallow waters of 18 to 36 metres deep, however, installation of the turbines is easier than other far-offshore projects. The plans were developed by a consortium building the project – dubbed Forewind but made up of large energy providers SSE, Equinor (formerly Statoil), Statkraft and Innogy – and were approved by the British government in 2015. Each of the three phases is set to provide about 1.2GW of power once complete, with that total of 3.6GW able to power six million homes. The entire £9 billion wind farm aims to be operational by 2026.

Though slow to ramp up, construction on cabling to connect the first phase has started with offshore work beginning in 2022 using the world's largest jack-up installation ship, which can lift 3,000 tonnes.[19] Such a massive vessel is necessary because Dogger Bank will use 200 of the largest wind turbines in the world. Each 2,800-tonne structure will be 260 metres tall, with a trio of 107-metre blades drawing a 220-metre arc through the sky.[20] Each turn of a rotor can power a house for two days, which is why behemoth blades atop towering turbines far offshore are the future for wind power.

Thanks to its terrible weather, the UK is a perfect candidate for wind energy, but turbines are popping up all over the world – on the mountains of the Swiss Alps,[21] the plains of India's coastline, and in the seas alongside Denmark – though it so far only makes up about 6 per cent of global electricity production.[22] As ever, China is the largest overall producer of energy from wind, though it makes up just 6 per cent of its total. But the world leader in terms of the proportion of electricity made through wind is Denmark, at a whopping 56 per cent, up from 12 per cent in 2000. The country has had a handful of days powered entirely by wind, and windy days mean it can make enough electricity to export some to its neighbours.[23] In 2020, the UK made a quarter of its electricity from wind, but aims to triple production by 2030.

Alongside being carbon-free operationally, wind turbines have one other major benefit: they're very cheap. Electricity from wind power is one of the cheapest out there – the 'fuel', like solar, is free, and although installation and maintenance costs do exist, they're cheaper than hydroelectric. However, turbines only turn when it's windy enough, regardless of electricity demand. That means other energy sources may need to be ramped up when the weather doesn't cooperate, and still weather has led the UK to power up coal plants, though that can be averted with storage technologies such as batteries or alternative sources such as biomass and hydro, as I will explore later.

Wind turbines have other downsides. Some people complain about the 'visual pollution' of the massive blades on landscapes, though others find them appealing – indeed, one study showed wind farms lowered house prices in some areas, but increased them in others.[24] Helpfully, their design means land can still be used for other purposes, notably farming. Noise pollution is perhaps more of a concern, as Scotland residents told WIRED it's 'like aircraft constantly circling overhead'.[25] Researchers say turbines may even be hampering birdsong.[26]

Indeed, a frequently mentioned concern is the impact on local wildlife, particularly with birds and bats flying into the blades, with one academic saying that installing wind turbines was 'akin to adding an apex predator to natural communities'.[27] Research suggests hundreds of thousands of birds were killed by wind turbines and their blades in 2012 in the US alone, with those estimates increasing to up to half a million as wind farms have expanded in America, though those figures are expected to be on the lower end.[28]

Alongside choosing better places to site wind farms to avoid migration routes and endangered species, researchers in Norway tested another simple solution: painting a single blade on each turbine black, in order to make them easier to see.[29] Because the turbines rotate quickly, the blades disappear in motion blur. By painting one blade a different colour, they're more visible, which helped to reduce bird deaths by 72 per cent.

Another looming challenge is the blades themselves, which are expected to last only twenty or so years – which means at the time of writing, the first generation of wind turbines will need replacing soon. While wind turbines are generally easy and low-cost to maintain, blade replacement could prove expensive. Furthermore, the blades are made of composite materials that are difficult to recycle, meaning two solutions are needed.[30] First, companies such as Enel Green Power are looking for ways to reuse the blades, such as grinding them up for building supplies; and second, startups such as Modvion are looking to build turbines and blades out of easier-to-recycle materials.

Due to these downsides it appears that the future of wind power will be massive and in the middle of the sea. Bigger blades and larger rotor diameters – the arc traced by those massive blades – means more energy can be generated from each installed turbine. Unsurprisingly, that has led to a steady increase in size. A report from the US Department of Energy (DoE) noted that in 2010 there were no wind turbines using rotors with a diameter above 115 metres.[31] Ten years on, nine in ten were above that size, with an average diameter of 125 metres – which the government department helpfully notes is 'longer than a football [soccer] field'.

Bigger blades generate more energy, but they also exacerbate the downsides of wind turbines: they potentially smack more birds out of the air, naturally cause more visual disruption and increase sound pollution. But many of the hazards of onshore wind could be mitigated by shifting offshore, with wind farms such as Dogger Bank, which offer more space for massive turbines and stronger winds to move those bigger blades.

Though more expensive for installation, offshore wind farms have the benefit of more regular, stronger winds – and that's even more true the further offshore they're built.[32] Plus, offshore farms avoid the difficult logistics of building onshore, including acquiring land, angering local communities and transporting blades on small, remote roads. 'Hauling wind turbine parts overland is restricted by how wide your roads are and how accessible the sites are,' says Dr Malte Jansen, of the Centre of Environmental Policy at Imperial College London. 'At the same time, economics dictates that you want to go bigger, because you get better [energy] production for the costs and materials.'

Of course, doing anything offshore is hard work – 'it's one of the most hostile environments you can imagine,' says Jansen. The energy industry does have experience withstanding North Sea storms, massive waves and salt-water corrosion thanks to offshore oil-rig platforms, which offer key lessons on how to fix structures to the ground deep beneath the waves. That said, such platforms don't have massive moving turbines swaying atop them. 'Even if they're idle, they're swaying because the wind just pushes them around,' he says. 'It's like a straw in the wind – if you were on top of one, you could feel the movement.' Of course, the water is also deeper, meaning most offshore wind turbines have been fixed to the bottom of the ocean, 50 to 60 metres below the water surface.

To go even further offshore, the wind industry is turning to floating farms. Ideas such as EDP's WindFloat Project[33] off the coast of Portugal or Equinor's Hywind[34] in Scotland mimic floating oil rigs, anchored to the seabed but floating in the water on a semi-submersible platform. The power is transferred back to the shore via an undersea cable. Because the winds are stronger and space is less of an issue, these offshore floating turbines are massive, with the blades of WindFloat more than 80 metres across each. That's huge, but nothing on Dogger Bank or what China has planned. There, a company called Mingyang Smart Energy is working on a 242-metre-tall behemoth with 118-metre-long blades and a rotor diameter the equivalent of six soccer fields.[35] Each turbine will be able to generate 16MW. These larger turbines and floating offshore farms are the future of wind power, Jansen says, though we need prices for parts and installation to fall first. 'It's a technology that needs to be proven, but there's no question it will work,' he adds.

However, as with hydro, wind power also benefits from shrinking down, as onshore challenges could be solved with smaller turbines and less-intrusive blades – or none at all. Consider Vortex. This Spanish startup has designed a bladeless turbine that captures wind energy through wiggling in the wind. A cylinder is fixed vertically using an elastic rod that allows it to oscillate in the wind; that movement is then captured by an alternator built into the stem, which turns the mechanical energy into electric current. 'The point for us here is the development of a wind turbine with a radically different approach to wind-power harnessing, not based on drag or other aerodynamic forces to get rotation on an alternator,' says co-founder and chief marketing officer, Jorge Piñero. 'If you eliminate rotation from the equation and you change it for oscillation by aeroelastic resonance, you have a wind machine that needs way less maintenance, has fewer energy leakings and is way safer for humans and birds.'

This means the Vortex may be well suited for urban areas or open public spaces, he says. A massive-bladed turbine may work best offshore, where it's all about raw power, but to reduce noise and increase safety, a smaller, unbladed version might make more sense. That said, Piñero notes that the appeal of Vortex isn't actually its smaller size, and that making a massive one would inherently mean it generated more power. 'In wind energy, the power you can harness by any machine grows squared by size and cubed by wind speed,' he says. 'Bigger wind devices are better in cost-effectiveness ratios. This is the same for us.' In other words, a massive wriggling Vortex could one day stand atop a mountain – but there's some work to be done first.

The company is currently installing 100 small beta-testing units at universities and research centres in Spain and elsewhere in Europe, South America and Japan. Alongside considering how to create larger versions, the aim is to better understand how the physics works and develop the industrial production process to improve efficiency. 'It is going to take a while until you will be able to get one of these wind devices at your local hardware store,' Piñero adds.

Challenergy is another bladeless design, known as a vertical-axis wind turbine (VAWT), with the wind catching on vertical flaps that spin around a central axis. That design makes it easier for the turbines to withstand super-high winds, which can cause problems for blade-style systems that need to be turned off when wind speeds are too high. And Challenergy's Magnus technology was created for some of the fastest winds of all: typhoons. The Tokyo-based startup believes such storms could be harnessed for energy in typhoon-prone areas that are too complex for standard wind farms.

When Typhoon Hagupit made landfall in August 2020, the company was able to test the prototype, which successfully generated electricity in winds as fast as 108km/h, while still staying operational. The Magnus is now being trialled in the Philippines, which sees three times as many typhoons as Japan, where it's hoped the system can handle wind speeds up to 252km/h to power a local microgrid.[36]

Another intriguing design comes via Icelandic startup IceWind. Like Challenergy's Magnus, rather than a trio of propeller-style blades spinning through the sky, IceWind has created micro wind turbines with sails that spin around a central column. Mounted in a frame or attached to another structure, the idea is that IceWind's turbines can be placed anywhere that backup power is needed, regardless of weather conditions – and that includes wind speeds as low as 2m/s.

The turbines made by Diffuse Energy, an Australian startup, are even smaller. Just a metre in diameter, the six blades spin inside a round case, making it look a bit like a stylish desk fan. Its small size means it can be installed almost anywhere, from off-grid homes to telecommunications towers, helping to keep communications up and running in emergencies.

Turbines don't need to be on- or offshore, they can also be airborne. Though they've struggled to gain traction, a few are running trials, including Kitepower, which generates electricity using a kite spiralling in a figure-of-eight pattern in the sky. MIT-spinout Altaeros, which makes helium-filled autonomous airships, trialled a variation in rural Alaska in 2020.[37] The Altaeros BAT is a giant inflatable turbine that floats at 300 metres, where winds are strong and consistent in order to turn the propellers at the centre of the doughnut-shaped blimp.

The shift to wind power is unquestionably going to mean massive three-blade propellers floating in the North Sea, but startups are showing there's plenty more room to innovate, in particular to reach rural areas and feed microgrids – be it with a wobbling stick, a metre-wide desk fan or a floating doughnut in the sky. The future of energy might be wind, but the future of wind is definitely a bit weird.

Solar

We get all the energy we need from the sun – or we could, in theory. Every hour and a half, sufficient sunshine hits the Earth's surface to provide the energy we need for an entire year, according to the US Department of Energy.[38] Of course, that doesn't work in practice, as to capture all of that energy we'd need to cover the planet with solar panels, but it highlights the potential of this technology. As of 2020, about 5 per cent of the world's electricity came from solar panels, but the International Energy Agency expects total solar capacity to increase 400 per cent by 2030, meaning its share is bound to grow significantly if we embrace this technology.[39]

The Atacama Desert stretches for 1,600 kilometres through Chilean mountains, plateaus and scrublands.

Considered the driest place on Earth, the average precipitation is 15 millimetres annually, though some cities and weather stations have never reported any rain. That makes it perfect as a stand-in for Mars in testing for NASA – the US space agency actually used the desert for developing tools for the red planet.[40] But the constant sun has also made Atacama the home for Chile's solar efforts with the Cerro Dominador solar complex, set on a desert plateau between mountain tops.

Cerro Dominador shows what can be achieved by harnessing solar power on a mass scale and by using different technologies. Solar panels are made from photovoltaic cells which generate energy when light particles called photons smack electrons away from the silicon material that most panels are made from, creating an electric current. Cerro Dominador has had 392,000 panels producing 100MW since 2017. The other type of solar power is from thermal panels that use the sun to directly heat water or other liquids, making them ideal for use in individual homes for hot water, though they're also used in large power stations. In this case, at the heart of the Chilean complex is a ring of 10,000 mirrors – it's a remarkable sight worth looking up on Google Satellite[41] – that focus the sun's rays onto a 250-metre tower to heat molten salt, which is used to produce steam to power a turbine. The thermal system went online in June 2021, generating 110MW to power 380,000 homes.

Solar collection can be on a massive scale – such as Cerro Dominador, or the 2.25GW Bhadla Solar Park in India, the world's largest – or installed cell by cell on individual rooftops, which is one route Italy is taking. The Mediterranean nation does have large solar farms, but until 2018 most of the nearly 10 per cent of the national electricity supply coming from solar power emanated from small rooftop projects.[42] While larger installations are catching up, the Italian government rebooted its tax break for small solar projects from 50 per cent to 110 per cent of the cost of eco-focused renovation projects in 2020, including installing solar panels on citizens' homes.[43] Overpaying for the cost of such work may sound odd, but the deal is that any surplus power produced by the solar panels has to be pushed back onto the grid for free. The initiative seems to be working: Italy has been the only one of eleven nations to meet an EU target to source at least 20 per cent of its energy from renewables by 2020.

There are, however, some challenges facing solar energy. One is the efficacy of panels. The amount of sunlight captured and converted by a photovoltaic panel depends on the materials, system design and where the panels are installed. In theory, silicon-based conductors can convert about 32 per cent of the sun's energy. In practice it's at most 22 per cent.[44] Another factor is the angle of the sun's rays. Sunlight is at its strongest when the sun is directly above a panel. At other times of the day, less energy can be harvested, if any at all. This is why solar panels often rotate or shift their angle to follow the sun, though that only improves the situation so much. It's also why countries nearest the equator have the most potential for solar power.

Another challenge is that building massive solar farms high in the desert isn't cheap or easy. Cerro Dominador came online after a two-year delay at a cost of $1.4 billion,[45] though costs of photovoltaic panels and molten salt technologies have reduced in the interim,[46] meaning it would now be cheaper to build. Another challenge has been the cost of panels, but the price of these has fallen dramatically, by about 82 per cent between 2010 and 2019,[47] thanks to China's efforts in mass manufacturing and a drop in raw material costs. According to the International Renewable Energy Agency (IRENA), in 2010, it would cost £800,000 to build a system to generate 213kW; that same price would offer 1GW now. Domestic systems also remain expensive, but that's largely because of the cost of labour for installation rather than the parts themselves.

Though solar farms are more efficient than smaller domestic systems, one of the criticisms of this technology is that it takes up land – and often the land that's best for agriculture, sparking competition between food and energy production. However, thanks to increased efficiency of panels, just 1 per cent of farming land would need to be converted in order to supply all the electricity for the entire world, academics at Oregon State University have said.[48] Even if more farmland is eaten up by solar generation, the two can actually work together. Italian utility Enel Green Power[49] is seeking to establish which plants and animals fare best in fields of photovoltaics, while researchers in Germany are considering propping up photovoltaics 12 metres into the air so that tractors and harvesters can attend to crops underneath. 'It doesn't completely cover the canopy, so there is still some light coming through,' Iris Lewandowski, chief bioeconomy officer at the University of Hohenheim, told WIRED.[50] 'The only difference for the farmers is that they have to make sure they don't drive into the pillars.'

The toughest challenge to solve is the fact that the sun doesn't shine 24 hours a day. 'It produces this diurnal profile that peaks at midday when the sun is at its highest point, and that's not particularly useful for an electricity system operator, as that's when demand dips,' says Jamie Taylor, a senior data scientist at Sheffield Solar, part of the University of Sheffield. Nor does the sun shine every day. In the UK, solar power could contribute as much as 30 per cent of electricity at any given moment, but an unexpected storm could suddenly send the bulk of that offline, meaning fossil-fuel plants need to be ramped up.[51] 'If you want to forecast it, you're reliant on a numerical weather prediction,' says Taylor. 'When they're asked to forecast irradiance, which is the key parameter when you're modelling solar, they can be wildly inaccurate.'

That means storage solutions need to be found, a topic I'll get to in more detail later. Electric cars have been mooted as one solution, repowering during the day to provide household energy at night – so long as you have nowhere to drive to in the middle of the night. Thermal solar systems, such as the molten salt tower in Chile, could also be the solution, as they essentially act as batteries to offer power when photovoltaics are no longer generating. In short, there are solutions to this problem but they are not yet widely in use.

So, what's next for solar? Beyond getting more solar panels installed on roofs, there are startups like Platio Solar who are looking to take solar integration a step further by cramming photovoltaics into every nook and cranny of our cities. For example, they are making paving slabs from photovoltaic panels, to produce pavements and walkways that generate electricity. And that makes sense: why pave drives, pathways and patios with concrete – a heavy emitter of carbon itself – that lies there useless when treadworthy solar panels can generate electricity? Platio make photovoltaic panels that are covered in load-bearing, slip-proof glass and framed with recycled plastic. The aim is to make use of existing areas, just as roof panels do, with the company saying that a 20-metre-squared patio of Platio could theoretically power a house for a year, though that naturally depends on local weather conditions and placement. The idea is being trialled in a park in Barcelona, Spain, with the local council looking to see if the panels are robust enough for city life.[52]

As with wind farms, solar farms can benefit from going offshore to solve the space issue, and giant floating solar farms are being trialled as a cheaper alternative to land-based installations – indeed, studies suggest that the cooling effect of water helps solar panels generate as much as 12 per cent more electricity.[53] Dutch startup Oceans of Energy builds floating solar farms – its first was in the North Sea, proving tropical climates aren't necessary – and it works with The Seaweed Company to farm seaweed alongside their solar energy generation.[54] Singapore has one of the largest floating solar farms so far – using the traditional measuring method, it's about 45 soccer fields in size – with 122,000 solar panels capable of generating up to 60MW.[55] The Sembcorp Tengeh Floating Solar Farm is designed to power local water treatment plants, and is carefully considered to ensure the panels don't disrupt the delicate aquatic balance, with gaps left for airflow and sunlight to reach into the water. Indeed, research[56] suggests that – if designed properly – floating solar farms may actually benefit the world's lakes by helping to keep them cooler, as climate change has raised temperatures and sparked problems like toxic algae growth.[57]

And then there are materials. Most solar panels manufactured today are made from silicon, limiting their efficiency at converting sunlight to power to an average 22 per cent. But other materials are being considered in the hopes of improving that conversion rate. One example is so-called perovskite crystals, which have a specific cubic structure that can be synthetically made at lower temperatures than silicon, and in theory could be up to 50 per cent more efficient. An early prototype from startup Oxford PV trialling a combination of silicon and perovskite already topped 27 per cent in 2018, but more work is needed. As an added bonus they can be printed very thinly, so they could be useful for getting solar panels everywhere from cars to clothing, letting us generate solar power anywhere. The panels can also be made flat black, rather than the shiny blue of current panels, making them stand out less on rooftops.

Better solar panels covering more of our planet means cleaner – and cheaper – electricity. That's a future of energy worth working towards, but there's more to renewables than hydro, wind and solar.

3

What's next: geothermal, biomass, wave and tidal – and more

Tunnelling into the Earth for its heat, burning leftover wood chips and unwanted trash, capturing the rise and fall of tides and waves – and even our own footsteps. These techniques could be the next generation of secondary sources of renewable energy, helping to balance the intermittency of wind and solar with more consistent power while taking advantage of natural energy that's currently going to waste.

Right now, such sources of power are little used globally, making up just 2.5 per cent of the world's energy mix. But countries with the right natural resources – be it volcanoes or endless shorelines – have leaned harder into these ideas and found real success. Here's a sneak peek at the next generation of renewables that could help make our energy mix even greener.

Geothermal

East of Reykjavik, the Hengill volcano stretches across 100 kilometres of green, rocky landscape in southern Iceland, dotted with steaming hot springs, criss-crossed by hiking trails – and a network of pipes. They sprawl from two geothermal plants, Nesjavellir and Hellisheiði, the latter dramatically spewing steam into the cool air at the base of the volcano.

Opened in 2010, Hellisheiði pulls steam from deep underground using hundreds of wells that stretch kilometres deep into reservoirs of hot water at 280 degrees Celsius.[1] These allow the island nation to take advantage of its geology to power turbines on the surface and generate 303MW of electricity, as well as send hot water 26 kilometres to the capital city, giving Reykjavik not only fossil-free energy but pre-heated showers too.

This isn't a unique experiment in the country. The bulk of Iceland's energy, some 85 per cent according to the government,[2] is from domestically produced, sustainably generated sources, with that last 15 per cent mostly fuel for transport. Geothermal makes up two-thirds of its energy, thanks to its use of powering turbines like those at Hellisheiði, while Iceland's electricity is generated almost entirely through a combination of hydroelectric (73 per cent) and geothermal (27 per cent). By tapping natural resources in a sustainable way, Iceland has become the world's largest green energy producer per capita, at 55,000 kWh per year, per person, versus the EU average of 6,000kWh. Plus, ditching oil and gas has helped the country's economy, no longer leaving it at the peril of international prices, and saving it $8.2 billion since the 1990s.

Iceland may be a small, sparsely populated country with dramatic natural resources – and 130 volcanoes – but its success in tapping its own unique landscape for sustainable power is being gradually echoed elsewhere as more energy is produced using similar techniques in the US, Indonesia, the Philippines and Turkey. And the idea is underused, a fact the Icelandic government is hoping to change by supporting the development of similar systems along the shifting plates of Africa's Great Rift Valley – in nations such as Kenya, Rwanda and Uganda beginning in 2010 – and expanding the idea to the East African Rift System.

But geothermal energy sources don't necessarily require a dramatic landscape: ground-source heat pumps take advantage of the warmth inherently in the earth below us, tapping it to produce hot water and home heating. It's a simple idea, treating the ground below us as a battery for warmth. Pipes of pressurised liquid – normally water with added antifreeze – are run a few metres below a building into the warmer ground. There, the principle of thermodynamic equilibrium means the heat is drawn into the colder liquid, heating it up naturally. A pump then returns that now-hot liquid to surface as hot water or to heat homes – it's Iceland's Hellisheiði, in miniature. In the summer, heat pumps work in reverse to push heat out of the building by pulling it into the now-cooler ground to be stored for winter.

The idea has sparked a swathe of startups, from Thermondo in Germany to Dandelion Energy in the US. Kathy Hannun co-founded Dandelion Energy after a career evaluating projects for Google X, the tech giant's innovation labs. She shifted to heat pumps because, despite showing so much promise as a heating technique, they're massively underused. So far, heat pumps make up just 5 per cent of residential heat demand globally, according to the IEA.[3] That includes air-to-air versions, which work by taking air from outside the house and compressing it to boost its temperature; it's sort of like a refrigerator run in reverse, but it does require electricity to run. The idea is increasingly popular in Europe, with Estonia, Finland,

Norway and Sweden all boasting twenty-five heat pumps sold per 1,000 households each year, though again that includes air-to-air models. Ground-source heat pumps are most popular in Sweden and Germany, though sales remain in the tens of thousands annually.

The main benefit of this technology is that, if you go deep enough, ground temperatures are relatively stable regardless of the weather, offering heating and cooling year round. So why aren't they better used? Though systems are cheap to use, they're expensive to install. 'It's been a luxury product for the very wealthy in the past,' says Hannun. If a customer pays up front for installation and the system, return on investment takes about seven or eight years with Dandelion, Hannun says, though that does depend on individual requirements. That's partially because it involves so much tunnelling, but also because contractors putting in a system have had to guess how much piping would be required, and to ensure the house gets enough heat they overinstall. Plus, the equipment to drill and install pipes has traditionally been too large for many suburban gardens, an issue Dandelion has overcome by investing in miniaturised equipment.

Houses also aren't designed quite right for heat pumps to be truly efficient. Heat pumps operate at lower temperatures than a boiler or furnace, which means larger air ducts or radiators are required in order to fully heat a space; plus, electrical upgrades might be required. 'Retrofitting buildings to heat pumps ... can be very complicated and expensive,' she says. The company is now working on ways to boost the temperature of its heat pumps to sidestep such issues. 'Getting to hotter temperatures and having an electrical system compatible with what we find in older homes will mean you can just take out a furnace and put in a heat pump – and if we make it that simple, it will really lower the barrier to adoption.'

It's an effort worth making. Switching to heat pumps means removing gas or heating oil from the energy mix – though as they still use electricity to power the pump that shifts the liquid from a home into the ground and back again, their carbon intensity will still depend on the local electricity mix. Hannun says the energy used to heat your home would be made up by roughly a fifth of electricity (used to power the pump) with the rest carbon-free geothermal.

Shifting to heat pumps will take investment, further technological development, and time – not to mention plenty of digging. But Hannun argues that even with those hurdles it's an idea that makes more sense than natural gas. 'Why is it right now cheaper and easier to extend an underground pipe with flammable, explosive and poisonous gas to a house and then have a machine that lights it on fire?' she asks. 'Why is that easier and less expensive than just putting some plastic pipes in the ground and having a heat pump? When you think about it that way and really take a step back, it's clear that decades of experience and investment and acceptance are behind fossil fuels, while the electric solution is still relatively new.'

Biomass

Biomass is one of the most-used sources of energy in the world – it's simply burning natural materials as fuel. That includes using wood or charcoal for cooking on a stove or heating a home, but these materials are not only a major source of greenhouse gases but deeply unhealthy for people. The biomass materials that have been touted as sustainable alternatives to coal are effectively the same, but biomass plants will add carbon capture systems to reduce the amount of emissions being released into the atmosphere, such as filters or other chemicals that will absorb the CO_2.

When Drax Power Station dropped coal – or mostly dropped coal – it originally wanted to replace that dirty fuel with another carbon emitter, gas. Instead, the UK power plant shifted to biomass, burning compressed wood pellets made from bits and pieces of wood left over from the timber and furniture industry in the US, Canada,

Brazil and Europe. So instead of burning coal to move its turbines, the plant burns leftover wood. There are other power plants that use compressed wood pellets, though they can also burn through waste food or specifically grown 'energy crops'. Those include corn, which is more often used as a biofuel in transport.

Burning materials may not seem particularly sustainable, but the argument put forward by the industry is that biomass materials are naturally carbon neutral. When trees grow, the argument goes, they sequester carbon; while they do release it when burned, if well balanced, the entire sequence would be carbon neutral as the trees that have been coppiced for timber or furniture would regrow and remove as much carbon from the atmosphere as had been produced by burning the old wood. In addition, such systems claim to use leftover or waste wood, which would need to be disposed of in another way, be it burning or landfill. When paired with carbon capture – as is happening at Drax in the UK – this method of generating electricity has been called carbon negative. Critics disagree, calling Drax's biomass burning 'greenwashing' – and the argument is sound.[4] After all, Drax's carbon dioxide emissions totalled 19.4 million tonnes, of which 13.2 million tonnes was from burning biomass. That should come as no surprise to anyone who's choked on smoke sitting alongside a campfire; it doesn't matter where the wood comes from, it's clear that burning it isn't exactly a clean fuel. The company argues that 'emissions from using biomass to generate electricity are balanced by the absorption of CO_2 from the forests that are growing'.[5] However, critics argue that this theory that all emissions are balanced by forest regrowth assumes that forests are well managed in order to avoid deforestation. Although Drax uses waste wood rather than felling fresh trees to burn, its supplier Enviva has been accused of harvesting trees rather than collecting leftovers.[6] If deforestation operations are used and new growth is not encouraged then the carbon emissions would approach those of fossil fuels.

Either way, the argument is that biomass is better than the coal that was previously used, though that is the same point used for natural gas, and better is not necessarily good enough. In this instance, if Drax's claims are correct, it at least makes use of material that would be unused otherwise – and that's behind the idea of using waste for energy.

Burning waste for power is equally controversial, though most of the time it isn't done with as much aplomb as the Danes have managed. Along the waterfront neighbouring Freetown Christiania in Copenhagen is an unexpected mountain. Designed by famed architect Bjarke Ingels, Amager Bakke, also dubbed Copenhill, rises up 85 metres, offering 450 metres of dry ski slopes, climbing walls and hiking trails – as well as clean energy from burning the Danish capital's rubbish. After being sorted for recycling, the remaining refuse from Copenhagen and surrounding areas – as well as further afield – is hauled to Amager Bakke to be burned inside the false mountain at 1,000 degrees Celsius, with the heat used to produce steam to turn turbines in order to make electricity as well as to provide home heating, all happening safely beneath the hiking and skiing trails. That means Amager Bakke not only helps improve the local electricity mix, but also reduces reliance on fossil fuels in homes.

Burning waste naturally produces harmful emissions, so this facility features a series of filters to remove pollution, including a system called Selective Catalytic Reduction, which reduces nitrogen oxide into its core components, leaving behind nitrogen and water – it's not wholly dissimilar to catalytic converters in some cars. The smoke leaving the stack isn't perfectly clean – still including nitrogen and carbon dioxide – but it's at least cleaner than fossil fuels.

There are other issues with the plant. If plastic slips in, more carbon emissions slip out. Its massive size requires waste to be imported for it to run properly, and critics have noted that means otherwise recyclable materials are often used.[7] And when shipping in waste from other countries, for example the UK, doesn't supply enough material to burn, the incinerator uses biomass. Incinerators such as Amager Bakke also make less sense in countries with a good energy mix where alternatives already in use are more sustainable, as is the case in Denmark. But they could be one solution to the landfill problem, which not only wastes valuable land but can produce harmful greenhouse gases such as methane.

Turning waste into energy need not require a city's worth of rubbish, a big-name architect or the creation of an urban ski hill, though. SEaB Energy installs miniature waste-to-energy plants inside shipping containers for office towers, hospitals, housing developments and more, where organic waste can be dumped in and be turned into a biogas similar to natural gas (as in methane) to produce electricity and heat.

The company has two products: the Flexibuster™ for between 500 kilogrammes and 2,500 kilogrammes of waste a day and the Muckbuster® for doing the same with farm waste such as manure. Both are anaerobic digesters, which are systems closed off to exclude oxygen that use bacteria and other microbes to break down organic matter into fertiliser and biogases. 'We've made it so that it's very easy to operate – just load the waste into the hopper, press a button and the macerator will run,' spokeswoman Bianca Sassow explains. Tipping in 500 kilogrammes of food waste a day generates enough heat and electricity for about sixty households, though Sassow says how much energy comes out depends on what goes in. That energy is then used locally or returned to the grid.

SEaB's system has limitations, notably in terms of scale, as it isn't economically viable below 500 kilogrammes a day. 'It's maybe not right for a single apartment building, but it could work for three apartment buildings next to each other,' Sassow says. So far, customers include Portuguese supermarket chain Continente, which throws away 182 tonnes of out-of-date and damaged fresh foods, generating 56MW of electricity annually.

Beyond generating your own heat and electricity, such systems keep that waste from heading to landfill, where they rot and produce methane. Even if your local area has compost collection, larger anaerobic digesters are less efficient, says Sassow, and using waste locally means it doesn't need to be collected by emissions-spewing trucks to be hauled to the edge of town. 'A huge amount of emissions is eliminated with decentralised waste management,' she says.

Tidal and wave

Southwest of Seoul is Sihwa Lake. It's not really a lake. Rather, it's the result of a failed experiment by the South Korean government to partition off Gyeonggi Bay across from Incheon airport with a 13-kilometre seawall in the hopes of turning it to fresh water for agricultural use. The plan didn't work and instead the seawall was converted to a tidal power plant. Twice a day at low tide, the sluice gates along the seawall are closed, keeping the reservoir at a low water level. As high tide hits, the water flows into the fake lake through ten turbines that generate up to 254MW.

Tidal systems may sound more akin to hydroelectric sources of power. But the way they work is actually closer to wind power, since they operate through turbines installed in the seabed underwater. When the tide comes in and out, the motion of the water against the blades turns the turbines. Different manufacturers use slightly different approaches. Sihwa Lake plant operates in only one direction: when the tide comes in, the gate holds the reservoir at a low water level so that the surrounding sea's water level is higher, sending water through the generators.

The technology comes with challenges similar to those seen with wind power: the equipment is difficult and expensive to install, the turning blades can injure wildlife, and underwater noise can disrupt animals. Larger systems, in particular barrages, can be destructive to sensitive tidal ecosystems, a fact noted by environmental activists who successfully halted an even larger tidal power station from being built at Incheon in South Korea. Such complaints were largely avoided with Sihwa Lake, as the local ecosystem was already in poor condition thanks to that failed government experiment.

Such challenges mean that while the technology has been in use since 1966 in France, with the Rance Tidal Power Station, just a handful of major tidal power plants have been built elsewhere, though systems have been proposed in the UK and Russia, meaning this could catch on in the future. Tidal power remains an idea in development, with the best design and format still to be decided. On the other hand, tides are more predictable than, say, wind patterns, meaning the amount of power generated is more consistent.

Wave power uses a similar idea, but rather than set the turbines at the shore to capture tides, the turbines are normally offshore, capturing energy from waves and currents. As with tidal power, wave-based generators remain a nascent technology. The Aguçadoura Wave

Farm, north of Porto, in Portugal, opened in 2008, but technical and financial difficulties scuppered the project. Meanwhile, a £200-million investment over 15 years by the UK government failed to lead to any commercial projects. Still, development continues: Chile is trialling a wave energy converter in surfing hotspot Las Cruces, designed by Enel Green Power and managed by a local marine lab.

One of the main stumbling blocks is that sea-based generators are currently too expensive to be cost-effective, as, according to Inna Braverman, CEO of Israeli startup Eco Wave Power, all of the necessary equipment is held in a container at sea and must be robust and waterproof. Her company offers a solution to the offshore challenges by making floating turbines that are connected to shoreline infrastructure such as jetties or quays. As waves move the floats up and down, the pressure created spins a turbine. The first installation was an eight-float plant in Gibraltar, generating 5MW, followed by another in Porto, Portugal, spread across four breakwaters, and a third in the works at Jaffa Port, Israel. Significantly, shore-sited generators can have just the necessary components in the water, with the rest on shore connected by a cable. All of that makes onshore systems cheaper to build, install and maintain than offshore versions, Braverman argues. Despite this, plenty of offshore wave systems have still won investment, says Braverman, with the hope that problems would be solved and prices would eventually fall – but that's not what happened.

'What happened is that most of those [offshore] companies didn't live long enough to see a decrease in price,' says Braverman, pointing to a Scottish programme that broke down three days into operation, sinking $100 million in funding after a new buyer couldn't be found in 2014. Such failures have made it difficult for wave-power companies such as Braverman's onshore programme to get insurance, in turn making it harder to win investment and regulatory approval. In addition, offshore projects drew the ire of environmental activists because the machines can – like any turbine – disrupt local wildlife. Eco Wave Power's idea avoids these challenges by locating its systems on human-made infrastructure, such as ports and breakwaters, which have already disrupted the ecosystem. 'We take something that already interferes with the environment, and we turn it into a source of clean electricity,' she explains.

You'd need a lot of these smaller projects to create the massive amounts of electricity made by a single hydroelectric dam or tidal plant. For example, Eco Wave Power's Porto installation generates 20MW, versus 254MW at the tidal barrage on Sihwa Lake or the whopping 22.5GW at the Three Gorges Dam on the Yangtze. But these smaller ideas produce clean energy without flooding ecosystems, requiring masses of carbon-intense concrete, and with fewer risks from climate change. More installations would be required, but the potential is real. A report from the World Energy Council predicted that wave energy alone could produce twice the amount of electricity currently used. 'It's an extremely significant resource that is worth attention,' says Braverman.

Kinetic energy

The fourth floor of the Quayside building in Kowloon East, Hong Kong, houses a running track, so locals have both a safe, clean place to exercise and a view. But the indoor track has a special trick: for every step a jogger takes, each flooring tile creates up to 5 joules of electricity.

This is thanks to British startup Pavegen. Its triangular tiles feature three generators at each corner, which depress slightly with each step, spinning a flywheel to make electricity. The tiles work indoors (examples include the track in Hong Kong as well as Abu Dhabi airport in the UAE, an office in Romania and a supermarket in Poland) and also outdoors (at the Chelsea Flower Show in London, UK, and in a smart city development in Bangalore, India.) The technology relies on the same kinetic energy that is also generated from hydro, wave, tidal and wind projects: essentially, they all harness movement to produce power. Kinetic energy can additionally come from vibration, and as such is being exploited by companies that include ReVibe Energy and 8power, who fix small devices to industrial equipment not only to monitor its performance but capture the vibrations it makes and use the energy generated to power wireless sensors. Such ventures may never be sufficient to power the world, as Pavegen itself concedes, but they could well help reduce a slice of carbon emissions.

The startup Constructis, meanwhile, is harnessing the kinetic power of cars via tubes embedded in road surfaces that move up and down as tyres cross them. 'The downward motion is converted into rotational motion and we then spin up generators and produce electricity to store in batteries,' says Rich Helstrom, director of business development, explaining the batteries can be part of the in-road system or external, depending on local requirements. 'It's not a complicated device, it's mostly mechanical.'

The systems are designed for lower speeds, such as off-ramps and parking lots, but future generations could function at driving speeds if the tubes are sufficiently spaced to ensure that none are skipped over. 'You're not producing at maximum efficiency when you skip tubes,' Rich Helstrom explains. He adds that while the system is perfectly safe for motor vehicles, it poses challenges for cyclists: 'It'll be quite bumpy for a bicycle to drive over as it won't depress the tubes at all.' He points out, though, that the tubes can be retracted if necessary and be programmed to automatically retract at night to avoid extra road noise in residential neighbourhoods.

Constructis is in talks with transport authorities to pilot its kinetic energy harvesters in high-volume locations, be it roadways, toll booths, or parking lots. The electricity produced could be used to power traffic infrastructure or construction, or be sold back to the grid. In immediate terms, it has trialled its system in the US at seaside town Virginia Beach. Here storms frequently flood local streets, leaving them impassable to emergency services. 'When flooding comes, you use the energy [stored in batteries] to drive pumps and move the water off the roads for access to first responders,' Helstrom says. It's an intriguing solution to a specific problem.

All this may seem small-scale, but it's worth bearing in mind some of the advantages that systems such as Constructis and Pavegen have to offer. They don't require land the way onshore solar and wind farms do. They also produce power right where it's needed. 'You don't need expensive transmission gear to get the energy from Point A to Point B, the energy is right where it's needed,' Helstrom says. 'That means our system is suited for urban installations in busy cities.' To that extent, kinetic energy offers a useful way forward.

Nuclear fusion

Nuclear power isn't generally considered a renewable resource, though it is carbon-free at point of use so it can help with decarbonisation efforts. But there is a cleaner version of nuclear power that's being seriously studied and could be commercially viable in time to help reach net-zero goals in 2050.

Right now, nuclear plants are powered by fission, which involves splitting unstable atoms to release energy. That process works in terms of energy production, but leaves behind toxic byproducts and risks catastrophic failure, as the meltdown at Fukushima has shown. Nuclear fusion, on the other hand, aims to retain the energy production while reducing the risks. Fusion is the process of melding atoms together and is the same reaction that powers the sun and other stars. In theory, the process can also be kickstarted in the lab using lasers, and this will give off significant energy but not result in the toxic waste that is part of the process of nuclear fission. However, at present the science behind creating commercial and sustainable nuclear fusion energy is some way off. In August 2021, the National Ignition Facility at the Lawrence Livermore National Laboratory in the US was able to kickstart the chain of events, called 'ignition', that leads to nuclear fusion. But the power that went into firing the laser exceeded the power that emerged at the other end.

Nevertheless, progress is being made. 'The pace of improvement in energy output has been rapid, suggesting we may soon reach more energy milestones, such as exceeding the energy input from the lasers used to kickstart the process,' said Professor Jeremy Chittenden, co-director of the Centre for Inertial Fusion Studies at Imperial College, at the time of the experiment.[8] 'This is crucial for opening up the promise of fusion energy and allowing physicists to probe the conditions in some of the most extreme states in the universe, including those just minutes after the Big Bang.' Nuclear fusion on a commercial scale is, according to experts, some decades away, but the promise is nevertheless there.

Bringing it all together

None of the technologies described in this chapter will, in themselves, solve our energy needs. We'll need to combine them, use them alongside other approaches, and accept that there will never be a one-size-fits-all solution. Iceland may well have the geothermal resources to power itself. British Columbia in Canada has the rivers and mountains to generate 90 per cent of what it needs through hydroelectric plants. Most countries, though, will need to opt for a mix of renewable options if they are to reduce their reliance on coal, oil and gas. Combinations of approaches may be required, in any case, since it's sometimes necessary to use energy to make energy. Heat pumps, for example, require electricity to run – energy that could be supplied by, say, solar panels.

Indeed, such flexibility is essential given the very intermittent nature of these renewable sources of energy. If the sun isn't shining or the wind isn't blowing, hydroelectric or biomass power will have to step in to fill the gap. On the plus side, when one source of energy is producing more than is required, it can be channelled into supporting the future production of others: excess wind-sourced power, for example, can be used to pump water into storage for later use in hydroelectricity production.

That said, the best way to use excess power is to shuttle it out onto the grid to replace fossil-fuel-generated power elsewhere – and for that, the grid needs to be smart and connected.

4

Smart grids to power the world

When a severe winter storm hit Texas in February 2021, many people weren't ready for the snow, wind and unprecedented low temperatures that it brought with it – nor was the American state's power grid. Energy production from all sources was hit, with gas lines and wind turbines all freezing. But one of the main causes of the five-day-long outages that left millions without power was grid failure.

The low temperatures froze infrastructure that wasn't designed for the extreme cold – after all, Texas is better known for sunshine and hurricanes than winter weather, though climate change means that's no longer the case. The privatised grid also doesn't interconnect with other states, meaning high demand for heating couldn't be met by neighbours.[1] The state government has formally attributed 151 deaths to the storm and its impact, though researchers have suggested more than 700 people died during the power outages.[2]

The Texas storm demonstrates that making power is only one part of the challenge of building a renewable future for energy. Next, we need to figure out how to get electricity produced from wind, solar, water or whatever else, from the power plant to homes, businesses and cars. And for that, we need a bigger, more interconnected and smarter grid.

The grid is what takes electricity from a power plant and delivers it to your home, through a network of transformers and substations and power lines. But existing grids are often basic and were designed for one-way traffic from a plant to an end user, such as a home or business. It's usually fine for one big regional plant, but it poses a problem for distributed sources, such as solar panels on an array of roofs or a multitude of small wind farms. Grids also require the 'right' amount of power: too little or too much are both problems that require careful management to avoid.

And grids are, for the most part, localised within a country. They don't generally cross borders. That poses a real problem if you want to sell excess renewables to neighbours who aren't having a sunny day or haven't invested in shifting to new energy sources. Conversely, it leaves you vulnerable to deficiencies in your own network.

All this goes to demonstrate why electricity grids – not turbines or photovoltaic panels – are the key technology we need to master if we are to ensure the future of renewable energy. Unless we can improve them to the point where they can cope with the supply challenges that intermittent renewable sources pose – whether by upgrading to smart technologies, installing storage, linking up networks via interconnects with other countries, or building a regional supergrid – then those power sources are doomed to remain small-scale.

Smart grid

At its simplest, the grid is the infrastructure that transmits electricity to your home or business from a power plant, like the network of pipes that take water from a reservoir to your tap. The trick to a grid is management: the supply of electricity running across the grid must match demand, an idea known as load balancing.

Renewables pose a real challenge to grids and load balancing. Not only do intermittent production techniques, such as wind and solar, complicate consistency of supply, but local micro-power production (from solar panels on roofs, for example) may add unexpected electricity to the grid. Jamie Taylor, solar academic at the University of Sheffield, who has spent years building a database of microgeneration to help collect data on the way that home-based solar systems add energy to the grid, describes how conventional grids struggle to record renewable energy. 'There was no visibility of it,' he says of solar on the UK grid. 'So to them, it was showing up as an invisible reduction in demand, which creates a real headache.' Given that grids were originally designed to be a one-way system, this is perhaps not surprising.

The solution is more data and automation – and the creation of the smart grid: smart meters in homes; smart appliances that can detect when power is at its cheapest; digitally controlled transmission infrastructure that can automatically, and in real time, manage the flow of supply. It's the application of computing to grid infrastructure for better management, load balancing, reliability and whizzy tricks such as discounted prices at times of peak supply and low demand.

Octopus Energy, a British power company focused on renewables, utilises a proprietary technology platform dubbed 'Kraken', which automates industry processes such as pricing, and so allows Octopus to offer what it calls 'agile pricing'. 'When the energy price is cheap, which essentially means that there's lots of electrons on the grid ... probably because the wind is blowing or the sun is shining ... we can tell customers that tariff and say: if you're going to charge an electric vehicle, do it in these times,' says Zoisa North-Bond, CEO of Octopus's generation team. That means that customers get lower prices, that excess renewable energy doesn't go to waste, and that stress on the grid is alleviated.

That's just the beginning. Octopus has bought out its sister company, Octopus Renewables, which owns renewable generation projects in order to manage its own supply. Normally, says North-Bond, to overcome local objections, wind turbines have either to be placed far away from communities or donations have to be made to community projects. Kraken offers more immediate and relevant recompense to people living near Octopus's small wind projects in Yorkshire and Wales, since it can offer them direct discounts on their electricity supply. 'Our theory is that the cheapest electron should be the closest one – if the electron is travelling down the grid only a small distance, you should pay less for your energy,' she says.

The 'fan club' gives local residents 20 per cent off their bill, and further discounts via agile pricing if wind speeds surpass 130 km/h. 'If you did your energy-intensive chores during that time of the day, such as putting on the washing machine or charging your car, you could get as much as 50 per cent off on your bill,' North-Bond says. 'When the wind was blowing, you could look out your window at the local turbine and react.' Plenty of people signed up for the smart tariff system, and Octopus was contacted by more than 300 other towns wanting to plonk down turbines on local green spaces to benefit from such discounts. So much for NIMBYism.

Grids can be further optimised through the application of machine learning and automated processes that link power networks to smart appliances and electric cars. It's possible, for example, for an electric vehicle to be charged automatically at a time when electricity prices are at their lowest. Similarly, public charging networks can notify those who charge their vehicles in the streets when the cheapest time is to recharge. 'We're able to send price signals to customers to bring them to charge points,' North-Bond says.

All of this can be achieved in the UK even in the absence of a particularly smart grid. As North-Bond says, it shows the power of digital technology when applied to energy. 'To make it easier, and to really do some of this at scale, there definitely needs to be more thought around how electrons are tracked and traced through the system,' she says. 'It's something we do talk to governments about a lot.' There are other solutions to the challenges raised by intermittent renewables and local generation, and they too integrate best into a grid when it's smart.

Microgrids

Microgrids are small, localised distribution networks. For example, a community can install solar panels on roofs and turbines in parks, sharing that power via a localised grid. This is particularly helpful for remote regions that have no connection to a wider power grid, but there are also advantages to interconnecting microgrids to the main grid so that communities have backup in case their own systems fail – they can also potentially sell their excess electricity to a smart main grid.

Microgrids can bring electricity to places that don't have access to a national grid, smart or otherwise, and so in the normal run of things would either have to go largely without or rely on fossil-fuel generators. They are also much less expensive and complicated to set up than big national infrastructure projects. In this context, it's worth remembering that it took twenty-seven years for South Africa to move from an electricity supply that covered 20 per cent of the population to one that reached 80 per cent. It's therefore no surprise that countries such as Kenya, Somalia, Uganda and Tanzania are looking to microgrids to fill in gaps in their electricity provision. Some 13 per cent of the world's population doesn't have access to electricity, 66 per cent of whom live in sub-Saharan Africa. Put another way, 650 million people currently have to cook with biomasses that can harm them through inside air pollution, and keep lights on in the evening via polluting diesel generators.

PowerGen Renewable Energy is one company that is seeking to tackle this issue, with the aim of connecting an additional million people in Africa by 2025.[3] 'The utilities in sub-Saharan Africa are all loss-making, except for two,' says A.J. Grosenbaugh, PowerGen commercial development associate, the exceptions being in Uganda and the Seychelles. 'That means they don't have the ability to raise funding through their tariffs or being a bankable entity, so they really can't expand into areas that aren't electrified.' While some countries – such as Kenya – are managing to roll out electrical access more widely, others are struggling. Grosenbaugh notes that in Sierra Leone, for example, the electrification rate is just 26 per cent, and that figure falls to single digits in rural areas. 'It will be decades before the grid gets to certain places,' he says.

However, thanks to microgrids, local communities don't necessarily have to wait for the arrival of a national grid. 'We're at this point where we now have the technologies with smart meters and renewable energy, where systems can be distributed, they don't need to be connected to the grid or a centralised generation system,' Grosenbaugh says. 'You can install a minigrid today, rather than waiting ten years for a national utility to build out.' If and when the national grid does reach a localised microgrid, the two can be linked up, reducing local prices, adding resiliency to both, and, if supply allows, introducing more locally generated renewable power to the larger grid.

Each of PowerGen's microgrids uses solar panels to build 50- to 100-kilowatt systems that cover between dozens and hundreds of homes or businesses over a radius of a kilometre. Most of the power is generated through solar panels and stored in batteries. There is also backup in the form of diesel generators. Local homes and businesses can access the electricity via smart metering that tracks usage and pay as they go via mobile, or pay a local agent in cash.

One downside to small-scale systems is that they're relatively expensive. 'Our tariffs are quite a bit higher than nationally, which enables us to cover our costs,' Grosenbaugh says. 'It means we're always under pressure to reduce our tariffs because it can be very political.' That's one reason why subsidies, donations and other financial support from global organisations are so key to these projects.

It's also why rollout has been slow. According to a World Bank report, Asia currently has the most minigrids. In Africa, by contrast, where the need is so great, and where some $220 billion will be required to connect those without electricity, investment has so far totalled just $5 billion.[4] More encouragingly, the report also shows that local costs in Africa for the supply and installation of solar panels, smart meters and other key grid components has halved over the last decade.

Various ideas have been floated to further slash costs. Modularity Grid aims to simplify minigrids, standardising designs to make them easier to set up and manage using AI, so installation can take a day rather than months and costs can fall. 'Really, it's these prohibitive costs that we are trying to address,' founder Elizabeth Nyeko told WIRED, as rates for electricity on smaller grids can be double that of the national grid.[5]

Microgrids aren't just for rural or deprived regions. When Hurricane Ida bore down on the US state of Louisiana in August 2021, and millions of people in cities such as New Orleans were left without power after the grid failed amid the heavy rain and high-speed winds, the residents of one particular apartment building were able to keep their electricity running. St Peter Residential, which was built for low-income military veterans, includes a microgrid powered by 450 solar panels, with excess electricity stored in batteries in the basement parking garage. Beyond offering emergency power during such storms, the system also helps reduce electricity bills.[6]

That building may have stood out as something of a lone beacon amid the darkened streets of New Orleans after Hurricane Ida hit, but the technology that sustained it is becoming increasingly common. In the US, Home Depot has installed microgrids using Bloom Energy's fuel cells, which have helped the DIY retailer stay open amid heatwave-sparked blackouts.[7] Given that such storms are increasing in severity and number thanks to climate change, microgrids can help keep communities powered even when national grids fail.

Batteries on the grid

Another solution that will help to modernise electricity distribution and supply is storage. When energy is cheap and plentiful, as it is at high noon on a sunny day for solar, that power can be stored in a battery for use that evening when the lights are switched on and people cook their dinner and watch Netflix. Tesla's Powerwall, for example, is a home battery designed to pair with the company's solar roof panels. Excess energy is stored in the battery for use when the sun isn't shining. Some have suggested electric cars could also make good home batteries, recharging during the day to supply power in the evening, if needed; such an idea is being trialled by Hitachi on the Isles of Scilly.[8]

But existing batteries pose challenges, notably around cost and efficiency. While they work to efficiently store energy at a household level, they remain expensive to manufacture; a Tesla Powerwall costs just shy of £10,000 to install. In terms of using battery technology on a larger scale, Tesla's CEO, Elon Musk, won a bet in 2017 to install a battery system that supported a local grid on an industrial scale within 100 days, meaning the losing party, Australian billionaire Mike Cannon-Brookes, had to pay for the project. While the successful installation won headlines, the companies running the battery farm have since been sued by the Australian Energy Regulator for failing to supply energy to make up gaps in service from other plants, the intended purpose of the project.[9] That said, it's unclear as yet from the lawsuit exactly why the battery farm hasn't always worked, which might cause concern as other projects begin to come online to even out renewable supply in California[10] and England.[11]

As we use batteries more and more for transport, the resulting innovation and mass production means costs are already coming down, falling by as much as 70 per cent in the three years to 2018. New materials will transform efficiency, meaning batteries will likely have a larger part to play with stabilisation of grids in the future. At present, however, when it comes to storing electricity on a grid we do have other options: water and alternative fuels.

In the last chapter, I mentioned pumped storage, which uses electricity at times of oversupply to pump water back into reservoirs, to be used later to generate hydropower at dams. Given the advantages it offers, it's perhaps no surprise that it accounts for as much as 95 per cent of the world's energy storage. But, of course, hydro dams, as CEO Stephen Crosher of startup RheEnergise points out, have to be massive. There are therefore only so many places where they can be sited. It's for that reason that RheEnergise has turned to the challenge of producing pumped storage tanks that can work on a much smaller scale.

To achieve this the company essentially had two options. It could build its tanks very high up – a solution that carries with it its own challenges – or it could utilise a liquid denser than water. RheEnergise chose the latter approach, using water with a clay-like material suspended within it that allows the tanks to be 60 per cent smaller than they would otherwise have to be to create the same energy storage. The solution offers other benefits, cutting construction costs and reducing spending on such infrastructure as pipes. Crosher stresses that the fluid is non-toxic: 'If we did have a spill, it would be like a lot of clay in a field – you could go and walk across it and get very muddy.'

Above all, the efficiencies of the technology mean that it can be employed in hilly areas, rather than mountainous ones, and so closer to most cities and towns. Crosher notes that even though hydro projects account for so much of the world's energy storage, they can be located only in the 25 per cent of the world where landscape and rainfall meet the necessary requirements, 'But if you bring the fluid to the project, and require lower hills, suddenly the Middle East and Australia are great markets,' he points out.

While storage can help with local supply, there's another answer to excess electricity: letting other countries use it in times of low supply so that they don't need to burn fossil fuels. For that, we need a grid that's connected.

Interconnected grids

The UK and Denmark share a history and a future – and both involve Vikings. Like the boat-bound raiders in years gone by, the £1.8-billion Viking Link will traverse the 620 kilometres across the North Sea. That, though, is where the similarities end. The 1,400MW high-voltage DC cable, which will link the Bicker Fen substation in Lincolnshire with the Revsing substation in Jutland, will be buried in the seabed up to 600 metres deep. When the interconnect cable hits land in each country, it will continue underground 130 kilometres to substations in order to join the existing electricity networks.

Why do two wind-power giants need to join forces on the world's longest DC cable? The Viking Link will let the two countries share electricity almost instantly, offering resilience to their respective renewable power generation. If the wind isn't blowing in Denmark, it probably will be in the UK. The two countries conveniently have what's called 'low correlation' – that is, they're unlikely to hit high or low production levels of wind at the same time.

Not only that, but the Viking Link interconnector will simultaneously allow the Danish energy companies to sell excess electricity to the UK (where prices are higher), and give the UK access to Sweden, Norway and Germany thanks to Denmark's existing interconnectivity to those countries. Work is expected to be completed in 2023. Other interconnections either already exist or are well advanced – between the UK, Belgium, the Netherlands and France; between the UK and Norway; and between Great Britain, Northern Ireland and the Republic of Ireland. More are planned. As of 2019, 8 per cent of Great Britain's electricity has come via interconnectors, with two-thirds of that from sustainable sources, according to National Grid.[12]

The interconnects criss-crossing the North Sea are slowly building a supergrid called – and this is a bit less sexy than the 'Viking Link' – the North Seas Countries Offshore Grid Initiative, which aims to pool power sources, particularly wind, via high-voltage direct current cables between countries. That, in turn, the idea goes, could link up to a wider European supergrid that would connect the continent with renewable sources and consumer markets in North and West Africa, Turkey and beyond. That's particularly powerful when the interconnects cut across time zones or weather patterns, says Professor Catalina Spataru, course director of the University College London Energy Institute. 'You have different correlations between the electricity demand and supply ... with time differences and with Northern and Southern Hemisphere seasonal differences,' she says.

As regional supergrids connect up with other regional supergrids it's possible to imagine a day when the world's electricity is shared via a global grid. Back in 2016, for example, China unveiled long-term plans for a $50-trillion global power grid, dubbed the Global Energy Interconnection, whereby power would be provided across borders via a grid fed by everything from wind farms at the North Pole to solar farms at the equator. The bold aim is to have it up and running by 2050. Such a long-term target may prove optimistic, but the shared grid element designed to cross parts of Asia (including Korea and Russia) has already won supporters, including Japan's investment giant SoftBank.[13] Here, it has been suggested, a supergrid could be established that would link up to a mooted solar installation in Mongolia's Gobi Desert.

For such an ambitious project as a global grid, many things need to fall into place first. Key among them is fast cables – and big ones.

Big cables

The core technology behind big cables is high-voltage direct current (HVDC) transmission. Most transmission is currently done via AC rather than DC. The former refers to alternating current, which can switch between positive and negative electrons and moves in a wave pattern. The wave-like motion means it has traditionally been seen as a better option for travelling long distances and is, therefore, the type of current used in most power grids. DC refers to direct current, which moves in a straight line and is therefore more consistent, losing less energy as it travels. HVDC boosts the voltage of DC currents to achieve less wastage over long distances. Some power will be lost when the electricity is converted back to AC for use by homes and businesses, but 'if you go beyond 100 or 200 kilometres, then HVDC is the way to do transmission,' notes Peter Lundberg, global product manager at Hitachi Energy.

As noted earlier, the further offshore a wind farm is, the more potential it has for consistency and efficiency, but the power generated still needs to get to shore to be useful. Dr Malte Jansen, the wind expert from Imperial College London, says that anything within 80 kilometres or so of the shoreline can run on a normal AC connection, the same sort of transmission as standard power lines. 'None of this is trivial,' Jansen says, but the core technologies are well understood at least.

To go further offshore, it makes sense to flip the AC power generated by the wind turbines into DC, as that's 'less lossy' over long distances, Jansen explains. 'DC power will be absolutely essential for transmitting power from offshore wind in,' he says. Further developing and installing this HVDC technology to support higher voltage and enable electricity to travel longer distances is key to enabling offshore sites as well as a global grid. Without this otherwise prosaic-seeming technology, the vast potential of offshore energy generation cannot be exploited, and clean energy can't be easily shared.

Without a smart, interconnected grid, we won't be able to make the best use of electricity to power more of our world, be it electric cars or communities coming online in developing countries. In short, grids are the first step to electrifying everything – and that's what we need to do next.

5

Electrify everything

The fjords of Norway are epic and quiet expanses of water lined with trees and gargantuan cliffs, the very image of nature in its pristine form. Cutting across the deep, long Sognefjord, northeast of Bergen, is the *Ampere*, which will help the environment stay that way: a fully electric ferry that since 2015 has run the 20-minute crossing between the village of Lavik on the north bank and Oppedal in the south. The twin electric motors, powered by 10 tonnes of lithium-ion batteries, have helped avoid 570 tonnes of carbon emissions each year, while still carrying 360 people and 120 cars on each journey.

Others have followed in the *Ampere*'s wake. Elsewhere in Norway, the 139-metre *Bastø Electric* became the largest electric ferry in the world when it arrived in 2021, able to shuttle 600 passengers and 200 cars between Moss and Horten, the country's busiest ferry route.[1] Denmark, you'll not be surprised to hear, has its own electric ferry, *Ellen*, with passengers noting 'it's very quiet'.[2] And in Stockholm, Sweden, local tech company Candela has announced a superfast electric ferry that can travel at 55 km/h, without the noisy, polluting diesel engines, and, thanks to a hydrofoil design that carries the bulk of the boat out of the water, with very little wake.[3]

This isn't just a Nordic trend. Electric is the future of ferries, with Bangkok buying 200,[4] and Canada and America teaming up on electric-hybrid models for two of the world's busiest ferry routes[5]. The British city of Portsmouth is trialling its first electric ferry, replacing the diesel engine with batteries repurposed from Nissan LEAF electric cars.[6]

Why are electric ferries so intriguing? They're one of many signs that electric vehicles are no longer a possibility held back by battery development or other technical woes, but now the imminent future of transport. To most of us, electric cars are nothing new any more – who doesn't have a neighbour with a Tesla or hasn't taken a ride in a Prius on an Uber journey? – but that's only the first wave of electrification. Next up will be public and mass transportation, including buses and boats, as well as logistical transport, such as trucks and trains, and tourism – be it cruise ships or aviation. And it's not just about using electricity to get around: industry will shift to cleaner power to save costs and carbon – the former to support their bottom line and the latter to meet government regulations and consumer preferences.

Of course, electrifying everything is most beneficial in terms of decarbonisation when the local electricity mix is sourced through renewables, otherwise we risk burning more coal and other fossil fuels to meet the increasing demand. That's led to criticisms that electric cars aren't actually as climate-friendly as many assume, with multiple researchers suggesting that the combined efforts of making the cars and batteries and powering them via fossil-fuel-generated electricity actually meant they were worse in terms of carbon than standard internal combustion engine (ICE) models.[7] Volkswagen, for example, noted that one of its cars causes a bit more greenhouse-gas emissions than the diesel model of the same car, when taking the German electricity mix at the time into account.[8] However, that didn't hold true for other cars, notably the Golf, nor was it true for the wider European electricity mix, in which case the electric versions were definitely better on carbon emissions.[9]

Nevertheless, it does remain true that for the shift to electricity as fuel to have the impact we so desperately need, we must first not only increase the proportion of our electricity mix that's produced from cleaner sources, but also expand how much renewable electricity we can make overall. We also need this cleaner electricity to be accessible via upgraded grids that can handle the increase in demand, especially as superfast vehicle charging becomes more widespread.

But the shift to electricity as fuel isn't only about decarbonisation. It also reduces local air pollution, choking our cities and killing more than ten million people annually.[10] Indeed, if you've ever stood on the deck of a car ferry overlooking the smoke stack, you'll have seen how much pollution can be pumped out by a single ship.

Going electric can also reduce noise pollution. One of the criticisms of wind energy is the noise – recall the Scottish residents saying it was like living under always circling helicopters – but that sound wouldn't make a dent in most cities, where the rumbling of cars and trucks can be as high as 85 decibels, potentially causing hearing loss.[11] One study suggests the noise of traffic may even cause dementia.[12] And as more people move to cities, clearing the air of pollution is a move that's worthy even without the existential threat of climate change.

Electric cars – and trucks

Electric vehicles have unquestionably been politicised to be seen as lefty, woke or performative – after all, the first real success story was the Nissan LEAF, an environmentally focused name that suggests who the car maker believed would be enticed to buy the car. The mainstreaming of electric cars has likely been partially helped by Tesla's 'sexier' models – Elon Musk's various iterations have been named the Models S, 3, X and Y as an inside joke at the company.[13] There's now even an electric Ford Mustang, the most American of muscle cars. The Mustang Mach-E now makes up 2.5 per cent of Ford's sales, and stocks reportedly sell out 'as soon as they hit dealer showrooms'.[14]

While the Mustang is iconic in America, the top-selling vehicle in the country is the Ford F-150 pickup truck. That's been true for thirty-nine years straight, reflecting the country's love for such utilitarian trucks, be it for work, corporate fleets or personal use.[15] And now it's going electric: the F-150 Lightning arrives in 2022.[16] To convince internal combustion engine stalwarts, Ford has ensured the F-150 Lightning is a performance pickup, with a range up to 480 kilometres, a superfast recharging station, four seconds to go from zero to 100 km/h, and more torque than standard models.

In addition, because the electric motor takes up less space than the combustion engine, Ford has even managed to squeeze in extra storage under the bonnet, as well as electrical outlets, meaning the truck can be used to power tools or even your home in case of a power outage. 'We basically said, "What more could we do with electrification, where it could enhance our customers' lives?"' chief engineer Linda Zhang revealed.[17] 'And wherever we had that opportunity, we took it and went after finding the solution for it. It gives our customers more tools at the end of the day.'

Between such perks and performance, the Ford F-150 has captured positive reviews, with even President Biden declaring 'this sucker's quick!' after a well-publicised test drive.[18] The ensuing demand sparked Ford to double its production targets to 80,000 annually; that said, the company normally sells more than 700,000 Ford F-150s.[19]

Car makers aren't just following Tesla's lead when it comes to electric – they're being forced to develop electric models not just by consumer demand but by governments. Norway is banning all new diesel and petrol cars from being sold in the country by 2025, followed in 2030 by Denmark, Germany, India, Sweden and the UK. So far only ten million cars currently on the road are electric, making up fewer than 5 per cent of global sales annually, though that figure is growing steadily, up by 160 per cent in the first half of 2021.[20]

Again, we need the biggest car users on the planet to shift to electric – and in the case of China, that is actually happening. In the ten years from 2010, China went from effectively no new-energy vehicles – which includes plug-in electric, hybrid and fuel-cell cars – to just shy of five million.[21] Half of the electric cars on the world's roads are in China.[22] The country makes more electric cars than the rest of the world combined, and has 487 electric car makers working on models, many of them on the cheaper end of the market.[23] The Chinese government did slash subsidies for buyers, but flipped it to a mandate that 40 per cent of cars must be electric or hybrid by 2030.

On the downside, as already mentioned, this only reduces carbon emissions if electricity is made from renewable sources. As China's energy mix is 85 per cent from fossil-fuel sources, shifting all of its cars to electric will help reduce local pollution, but won't make as big a dent in decarbonising and may even increase the amount of coal burned in order to increase the electricity available.[24] On the other hand, by mass-producing cheap electric cars, they'll become more widely available everywhere else in the world, helping other countries hit their goals to ditch petrol and diesel vehicles within the next decade.

There's a challenge that comes with electrifying cars: how to charge them. Charging points are already being installed, but making them fast enough and ubiquitous enough to give drivers confidence requires real work. And that requires work on the grid, to ensure electricity can be pulled down quickly enough without stressing infrastructure – one reason we're seeing tie-ups between energy companies such as Octopus and charging point networks.

Public transport

Cars are but one form of transport that needs to go electric. Plenty of trains have managed to make the shift to electric power, with overhead lines providing energy, but that's not true everywhere. Indeed, the spiritual home of railways, the UK, has electrified just 38 per cent of its tracks, leading to a heavy reliance on diesel, especially for freight.[25]

Buses are also going electric, but it's not so simple as plonking a battery on board. Rolling out electric buses will need an army of electric-trained mechanics, lessons for drivers on getting the most out of batteries, and installation of superfast chargers.

However, even beyond decarbonising, there's plenty of opportunity to tip the scales: not only will electric buses help address local air pollution, but they open up new business models. Public transport hubs could become the centre of electric charging in towns and cities, argues

Mike Nugent, head of fleet strategy for Hitachi Europe. Right now, bus depots are often unattractive, greasy and closed off to residents. 'In the future, they're going to be lovely, clean, sparkly environments,' he says. 'They'll have electricity generated on site through solar PV, with battery storage on site.'

Bus depots take up a lot of space, so the idea is to build a large canopy to protect the vehicles, on top of which photovoltaic panels will capture solar energy. That energy can be used to refuel buses, sold back to the grid, or used for charging local residents' cars. 'The beauty of buses is they're going to be charging for six hours at night on a rapid charger – you've got 18 hours a day where all that power is not being utilised and can be by other people.' This idea was trialled at the Caledonia bus depot in central Glasgow during COP26 in Scotland.

The charge-sharing idea need not be kept to public transport alone, though it could help fund bus networks struggling with low ridership post-pandemic. Instead, any company or industry could mimic the bus depot idea and share out green electricity locally, Nugent believes. 'We see our solutions as being completely transferable,' he says. 'A depot could be a factory or a farm – anywhere that is using carbon-based electricity.'

Of course, not everywhere is ready to switch to electricity, so alternative fuels will be needed to decarbonise transport, home heating and industry – but biofuels and hydrogen could help fill that gap.

6

Alternative fuels

At 10:36am on 15 September 2021, British Airways flight BA1476 departed London's Heathrow airport, landing at Glasgow 554 kilometres to the north less than an hour later. It did so using sustainable aviation fuel (SAF) partially made up of recycled cooking oil. The demonstration was part of BA's 'Perfect Flight' decarbonisation programme, and this latest attempt slashed carbon emissions by 62 per cent versus a decade ago.

Slightly fewer than half of those reductions are because of the biofuel used, with the rest down to other changes: the Airbus A320neo used for the flight is a fifth more fuel-efficient than the plane used in 2010, while BA has slashed aircraft weight by installing lighter seats and removing inflight magazines – every little helps. Electric ground vehicles at the airport and planning a more direct flight path without having to take up a holding pattern over Glasgow were also used to shave emissions further.

Simply taking the train instead of this short-haul flight would have prevented even more carbon emissions, but such changes to our behaviour, as well as advancements in fuel efficiency and the fuels we use, will all be necessary. The transport of people and goods makes up a quarter of the world's energy footprint, and most of that is currently powered by petrol or diesel.[1] As we saw in the last chapter, while electric vehicles are one way to clean up cars, lorries and public transport, we aren't yet – and may never be – capable of powering shipping or aviation with electric batteries, as the weight-to-energy tradeoff required may mean they're simply too heavy to ever work. And that's a problem, as shipping and other marine transport makes up 2.5 per cent of global emissions[2] – about as much as Germany or Japan[3] – while aviation makes up about 2 per cent.[4] This means that, in many cases, alternative fuels may be the best solution to reduce emissions.

Changing either industry isn't simple, as ships and planes take ages to design, win regulatory approval and be manufactured, and stay in use for much longer than cars or lorries. For all these reasons, finding alternative fuels to petrol and diesel isn't proving easy, but there are some solid ideas in the pipeline. Beyond techniques to reduce the carbon in a fuel, such as biofuels like SAF, alternatives such as hydrogen, methanol and ammonia could help mitigate the carbon impact of transport, heating and industry.

Biofuels

The sustainable aviation fuel (SAF) that powered that British Airways flight is a biofuel, which simply means it's a fuel made from plants or animal waste rather than fossil fuels. There's a wide range of biofuels already in use. Indeed, much of the fuel filling vehicle tanks in the US is E10, made up of a mix of 90 per cent petrol and 10 per cent ethanol, which is made from fermenting corn or other grains. The UK also recently shifted from E5 to E10. Many cars in Brazil can already run on pure ethanol, which in this case is often made from sugar cane.

The SAF that powered that flight between London and Glasgow is a blend of recycled cooking oil and animal waste fat sourced from renewable fuel maker Neste and oil company BP. The flight used a mix of SAF with standard jet fuel at a one-to-two ratio, slashing emissions by 28 per cent, though fossil-fuel giant BP says it's possible to increase the ratio of jet fuel to SAF to 1:1, with no changes to planes or refuelling systems at the airport.[5]

Yet just 0.01 per cent of aviation fuel used globally in 2019 was SAF. Why? It's roughly five times as expensive as standard jet fuel,[6] though that depends on the ratios used.[7] In addition, the supply of SAF from fuel companies simply isn't great enough to make regular use of sustainable fuels possible – and that is one area where government intervention may be necessary. 'The faster we scale up supply and use of sustainable aviation fuels, the faster we can decarbonise aviation and protect the benefits of flying in a world without carbon,' said Heathrow airport CEO John Holland-Kaye in a statement following the demonstration flight.[8] 'What is needed urgently is for government to introduce policies to increase the supply of SAF and to provide the right price incentives for airlines to use it.'

Matt Finch, policy director at think tank Transport & Environment, agrees, noting that the first test flight using biofuel mixes in aviation took place back in 2008, sparking predictions at the time that by now the industry would be 10 per cent fuelled by SAF. 'Governments sort of said: okay, this is good, we'll leave you guys to it,' says Finch. 'But in fact, it's now about 0.04 per cent.' In response, governments have introduced mandates stipulating that fuel firms must start offering a better supply – the UK is consulting on requiring flights leaving the country to use 10 per cent blends by 2030, while the EU is considering introducing a 2 per cent requirement in jet fuel by 2025, climbing to 63 per cent in 2050. That has led to some investment in production, Finch says.

There are other challenges. If a biofuel-based alternative such as SAF does become widely used in aviation, high demand could spark a shift away from waste materials to actual feedstocks – in other words, we'll stop burning recycled and waste materials and start raising crops just to be jet fuel rather than food. 'The main bottleneck for the expansion of biofuel is the availability of the feedstock, because we only have a very limited amount of waste cooking oil and animal fats,' says Dr Hu Li, associate professor at the University of Leeds. 'We are in an ethical debate for years that we shouldn't use anything crop-based because that's competing with food for the land.' There are potential alternatives, including seaweed, algae, grasses and even leftover wood materials to make cellulose-based ethanol, but having enough of any one type is continuing to prove a challenge.

For this reason biofuels are not going to be in plentiful enough supply to clean up all forms of transport, so that means we should focus its use on the area where it makes the most impact, and that's likely to be aviation, says Li. Cars and trucks can go electric more easily than planes, while marine industries are exploring other alternatives. 'The aviation sector is harder to decarbonise than other sectors, and will need liquid fuel for the near future,' says Li. 'We don't have any possible replacements for jet fuel. I think the consensus now is we should reserve biomass for the number one problem, and give it to aviation.'

As Matt Finch points out, 'Getting SAF into the mix faster is a bit of a no-regret policy.' He points to contrails, noting that the white streaks left by planes in the sky have a larger impact on global warming than carbon emissions from fuel.[9] Using biofuel does help reduce contrails, meaning every bit of cooking oil that ends up as jet fuel can have even more impact. He also points out that there are other things we can be doing to combat aviation's carbon footprint. Contrails form in certain weather conditions, and a plane can just fly higher or lower to avoid that weather. 'Sometimes it's honestly just that simple,' he argues.

However, there's more to biofuel than powering transport. It is estimated that 40 per cent of global carbon emissions come from heating homes and businesses, with another 21 per cent coming from industry.[10] Switching both to electric power generated by renewables is one answer, but faster results could come from supplying cleaner fuels. For that, biofuels could be one answer.

One example of the many ways you could do this is evidenced through the British startup bio-bean, which uses leftover coffee grounds from factories, coffee shops and office blocks to heat homes and power machinery. Once collected, the grounds are treated, dried and compressed, creating burnable pellets for industrial biomass boilers and 'fire logs' for home wood burners and stoves, which like any biomass does still cause emissions when burned, but keeps the material out of landfill where it gives off methane. 'The coffee pellets displace the need to use virgin timber and reduce reliance on imported pellets,' says

Jessica Folkerts, bio-bean's head of marketing. 'They exploit coffee's high calorific value, burning more efficiently than kiln-dried wood logs, and provide a sustainable alternative to coal or mass-imported wood logs.' The idea shows that it's possible to leave oil in the ground and power homes, businesses and even cars with waste resources.

A point to remember is that burning biofuels, including used cooking oil or coffee logs, still causes carbon emissions, though using a waste product that was otherwise going to landfill is naturally better than excavating fossil fuels from the ground. In short, sustainable aviation fuel is better than standard jet fuel, but may never fully solve industry's carbon emissions. For that we will need to look to new kinds of fuels, such as hydrogen or ammonia.

Hydrogen

Hydrogen is the fuel that's leaving biofuels in its wake – in this case, literally. The *Europa Seaways* ferry will set sail by 2027, and if all goes to ferry company DFDS's plan, rather than a smokestack spewing plumes of pollution as it churns the 480-kilometre journey from Copenhagen to Oslo, it will have a deck-top fountain entertaining passengers with its emissions. That journey currently burns 35 tonnes of dirty oil over the two-day trip, but this ferry will use hydrogen fuel cells instead. This same idea is being touted for passenger cars.

Europa Seaways answers a call by the EU for zero-carbon ship designs by 2030. As the ferry will leave behind only clean water on its picturesque journey – as that's the only material emitted from using hydrogen as a fuel – one suggestion from a customer competition of what should take the place of the ship's smokestack was a massive fountain. 'It would be a good way for us to communicate what this is about: that you can actually propel a 200-metre ship and the only exhaust is clean water,' Jakob Steffensen, director of innovation at DFDS, told WIRED.[11] 'I would love to show my kids that.'

But there are two problems with hydrogen: we don't yet make enough of it, and it's not always clean. There are myriad ways to produce hydrogen, but two that concern us. Hydrogen can be easily made from existing fossil fuels, such as natural gas or diesel, by applying steam at extremely high temperatures, a process known as steam reforming. The vast majority of hydrogen[12] that is currently made uses steam reforming on natural gas, giving off 9 tonnes of carbon dioxide for every tonne of hydrogen produced, thanks to the fossil-fuel ingredients and energy-intensive process.[13] When paired with carbon capture and storage (CCS) – where the emissions are mostly prevented from escaping into the atmosphere – that type of hydrogen is commonly known as 'blue' hydrogen; if no CCS is used, it's dubbed 'grey' hydrogen.

The second technique for making hydrogen is better, replacing fossil fuels as core ingredients with plain old water. This idea uses electrolysis, which applies energy to a water molecule to knock off the correct atoms to make hydrogen. An electrolyser, the machine used in the process, is like a battery running backwards. Rather than combining materials to create electricity, electricity is applied to one material, in this case water, to create another, hydrogen. This is called 'green hydrogen' and is particularly environmentally beneficial when the energy used for electrolysis comes from renewable sources. And it need not requisition fresh water away from drinking supplies: researchers at Stanford University have created a system that can electrolyse saltwater.[14]

But electrolysers and clean energy plants to power them still need to be built. That's one reason why blue hydrogen continues to be used, as a stepping stone towards a more sustainable version – similar to how electricity plants ditch coal for natural gas as they carefully move towards decarbonisation. But that may not be wise. Researchers from Cornell and Stanford Universities suggested that blue hydrogen may be worse than grey hydrogen, diesel oil or even coal in terms of greenhouse gas emissions, because the process not only fails to capture all carbon but also leaks methane.

'Compared mass-to-mass, it [methane] is more than 100-times more powerful as a warming agent than carbon dioxide for the time both gases are in the atmosphere and causes 86-times the warming as carbon dioxide over an integrated twenty-year time frame after a pulsed emission of the two gases,' that paper notes.[15] 'Approximately 25 per cent of the net global warming that has occurred in recent decades is estimated to be due to methane.'

Despite these concerns, blue hydrogen continues to win government support, with the UK government investing £4 billion in both types, with much of the money going to fossil-fuel companies developing blue projects.[16] The Biden administration in the US is taking a similar approach, saying it would invest in projects that create hydrogen from fossil fuels.

Why? Power plants to make the blue stuff already exist, making hydrogen at a lower price-point than the green variant, facts that are presented to government by lobby groups such as the Hydrogen Council and Gas for Climate. Both groups are funded by oil and gas players who stand to financially benefit from the continued use of fossil fuels to make blue hydrogen as well as sustainable energy subsidies. The debate is fraught: in the UK, the disagreement between green and blue sparked the resignation of the chair of the UK Hydrogen and Fuel Cell Association, with Chris Jackson writing in a LinkedIn post: 'I believe passionately that I would be betraying future generations by remaining silent on that fact that blue hydrogen is at best an expensive distraction, and at worst a lock-in for continued fossil-fuel use that guarantees we will fail to meet our decarbonisation goals.'

Transport & Environment's Matt Finch agrees that green hydrogen is a better option, but admits it will take work to build the renewable power plants and other infrastructure. 'We've got some existing facilities [that can make blue hydrogen],' he argues. 'We might as well use them.' He adds that carbon capture and storage used with blue hydrogen isn't perfect, but it's better than nothing.

Price is another complaint, as the new green technology remains, says Li, three times more costly than incumbent fuels, blue hydrogen included. That's largely because the required infrastructure, such as electrolysers, remains expensive, but as suppliers scale up production of necessary equipment and components, those prices are expected to fall, while better designs will lead to production efficiencies.[17] Another challenge is the cost of electricity to power such systems; as renewable electricity prices continue to fall, so too will the price of green hydrogen. Sebastian Koks, the CEO of Maersk-owned Green Hydrogen Systems, an electrolyser manufacturer, has said it will take at least a decade before green hydrogen can compete on price with fossil fuels – but then predicts it will become cheaper than diesel or petrol.[18]

But given many of the new blue hydrogen plants won't be online for several years, it may be worth investing in the green stuff. Denmark, it will not surprise you to hear, has a better and more timely plan.[19] Danish utility Ørsted's existing wind farms dotting Copenhagen's harbours will be used to power a 10MW electrolyser beginning in 2023. That means that the wind farm might not send all or even any of its generated electricity to the onshore grid, but instead put it to use producing green hydrogen onsite. That also solves wind power's intermittency issue, as you'd only produce hydrogen when power was available. Build an electrolyser alongside a wind turbine or any other renewables plant, and it can instead use any excess power to make hydrogen. That hydrogen can either be used as a fuel offsite or as a battery to power the grid when supply is low.[20] The first batch of green hydrogen at Ørsted will be used in local buses and trucks.

By 2027, a new wind farm at Bornholm Island, a bit further south of Copenhagen, will begin operation, enabling a 250MW electrolyser. That will allow more hydrogen production and will be paired with carbon captured from CCS elsewhere to produce methanol for AP Moller-Maersk ships and e-kerosene to be used as jet fuel for SAS and other flights out of Copenhagen airport. By

2030, if all goes to plan, Bornholm's wind farm will be fully up and running, enabling the electrolyser to be boosted to a whopping 1.3GW to supply more sustainable fuel.

The project is compelling as it brings together energy suppliers and buyers, growing supply and demand together. After all, there's no point making hydrogen if no one will buy it, and public transport operators can hardly fill their buses with green fuel if no one makes it. Denmark is working hard to orchestrate these industrial links to accelerate the viability of alternative fuels. 'There's a chicken and egg dilemma,' DFDS's Steffensen told WIRED, when it comes to supply and demand.[21] 'We think projects like [*Europa Seaways*] can help ... because of the big quantities of fuel that will be needed.'

There are other challenges to hydrogen beyond economics and production, notably that it is more explosive than other options – never a good characteristic for a fuel. 'The minimum ignition energy in air for hydrogen is 0.02mJ, in comparison, methane is 0.29mJ,' Charles Haskell, decarbonisation programme manager at Lloyd's Register, told WIRED. 'So in case of a leak, the probability of ignition is very high, thus additional safety measures are required.' That means ships must be redesigned to a higher standard to avoid hot electronics sparking a leak, while vents may need to be built throughout a ship's systems to avoid buildup of buoyant hydrogen.

Hydrogen's energy density is lower by volume than petrol, so more space will need to be set aside for fuel. That may mean trucks and cars need to be refilled more frequently, which is feasible if not ideal, but it doesn't necessarily work for a container ship traversing the entire globe – for that, alternative fuels such as methanol, biofuels or ammonia could be used. Nevertheless, the first hydrogen train, the Alstom Coradia iLint, hit the rails in Germany in 2018 for areas that can't be easily electrified with overhead cables, and has since been trialled in France, Sweden, Poland and Austria, with Italy ordering fourteen trains to carry passengers.[22] Airbus has started development work on hydrogen-fuelled planes with a range of 3,000 kilometres in the hope they'll be in service by 2035, just please don't mention the *Hindenburg*![23] Transport & Environment's Matt Finch isn't convinced by those timelines, however. 'I think we'll probably get hydrogen-powered planes, but not on the timescales they're saying,' he comments. 'Even if they stick to those timescales and have a plane ready by 2035, planes are kept for a long, long time – thirty to forty years. So you've got that problem of filtering it through.'

Hydrogen could also replace fossil fuels heating homes that are currently warmed by natural gas, or for cooking. Billions of people in the world still use biomass such as charcoal or wood for cooking, exacerbating deforestation and killing millions of people from indoor air pollution. Researchers are working on ways to produce hydrogen gas using solar power in rural communities in Ghana, Jamaica and Indonesia, either running the fuel in pipes to homes or distributing it in tanks similar to propane.[24]

Other fuels

The shipping giant Maersk is taking part in those Danish hydrogen production trials at wind farms, but the company has also ordered eight container ships from Hyundai Heavy Industries that will run on methanol, another carbon-neutral fuel.[25]

Green methanol is made by combining green hydrogen and carbon dioxide that's been captured from renewable sources. Like hydrogen, green methanol is still not being mass produced, though it is one of the fuels made in that massive Copenhagen harbour project mentioned on pages 147–8, with some of the green hydrogen going to produce methanol.[26] Maersk has also invested in California-based alternative fuels startup WasteFuel, in the hopes of scaling production of methanol. Helpfully, the ships that Maersk has purchased can run on standard fuel as well, in case there's not enough methanol to be had. 'We know that sourcing an adequate amount of green fuel for our methanol-fuelled vessels will be very challenging, as it requires a significant production ramp-up globally,' said Morten Bo Christiansen, head of decarbonisation for AP Moller-Maersk.[27]

The vessels, set for delivery in 2024, cost up to 15 per cent more than those that use standard heavy oil as fuel, but will help the company meet its 2050 net-zero goal. Plus, Maersk believes that its customers are willing to pay more for sustainable shipping, which they can do via its 'eco delivery' service.[28] That lets retailers, car makers and other Maersk customers buy a spot for their containers on a bio-fuelled ship – and then in turn include that in their own sustainability reports and marketing materials. 'We're in it for our customers … and thankfully they are very appreciative of this and demand is really growing,' Christiansen told journalists at a press conference.[29]

There's another fuel gaining ground in shipping: ammonia. Though challenges remain to make it work for shipping, the International Maritime Organization believes ammonia has potential, predicting it could make up more than a third of maritime fuel by 2050.[30] As with hydrogen and methanol, there are 'blue' and 'green' versions, with the latter made via electrolysis using renewable energy sources that would make it carbon neutral. And, as with both of those other fuels, there's a lack of manufacturing capability for the green stuff, though that will be boosted by a massive new plant in Australia.[31] Like hydrogen, ammonia comes with its own safety risks that will require modifications and redesigns to ships, especially as it's toxic to humans and corrosive to infrastructure. 'I'm not a chemist, but the businesses and fuel suppliers I've spoken to all say the same thing: ammonia is one of the most disgusting products you'll ever have to work with – and the main problem is actually the smell,' says Finch. 'The smell is sufficiently bad that if you ever spilled it, you wouldn't be able to go anywhere close to the spill. It's not like jet fuel, where if you spill it someone just goes along and mops it up.' Of course, oil is also rather problematic when spilled, just ask the Gulf of Mexico ...

Alternatively, ammonia fuel cells could be used, reducing the risks. Helpfully, researchers suggest ammonia could prove to be much cheaper in the long run than other emissions-free fuels.[32] No wonder then that ship makers are already working on developing engines that can use ammonia as a fuel, with a global consortium[33] working to build the first ammonia-fuelled ship and Finland's Wärtsilä[34] already testing its own engine, while others are working on ammonia fuel cells.

Whether such efforts will be enough to fuel the future of shipping – let alone everything else – remains to be seen, but there's plenty we can do to accelerate the energy transition, before we're left drowning from climate change.

7

Making it happen

Renewables are the future of energy – we just need to make the transition happen, and quickly. Though there are massive engineering challenges, the real inertia has less to do with technical hurdles than politics and costs.

Progress has been slow. Since 1985, the world's electricity mix has improved from 21 per cent renewables to 29 per cent, while the energy mix has grown from 6 per cent to 11 per cent. Much of that progress has taken place since 2010. Though hydropower still makes up 60 per cent of renewable energy, solar and wind have helped bend that line upwards on the charts.

Indeed, despite concerns that Covid-19 lockdowns would slow progress on renewables installations, 2020 saw the best growth in renewable capacity ever. 'There's a new normal coming up in the short term, which means that ... exceptional growth will become the new normal,' says Heymi Bahar, senior analyst at the IEA, pointing in particular to offshore wind as a 'bright spot'. That's the good news. But reaching net zero by 2050 doesn't just require that impressive growth to continue – it needs to triple. 'From "exceptional" growth to tripling is a challenge,' Bahar admits.

Researchers suggest that in order to shift to clean energy while meeting growing demand, renewables need to be installed at a rate of 2 to 3.5 times as quickly as *all* energy-generating infrastructure since 1985.[1] 'To meet climate targets, the rate of clean energy deployment required would be unprecedented,' says the Breakthrough Institute's Seaver Wang. Is that even possible? Wang's colleague at the Breakthrough Institute, analyst Jameson McBride, responds, 'That's the million-dollar question, and I don't think anyone really knows.' He points to the fact that the biggest decarbonisation of economies was actually in the 1970s and 1980s, when countries shifted to nuclear power and hydroelectric, rather than in the last ten years.

Wang points to China, which has impressively expanded its solar and wind capacity, doubling its installation rates over the last few years. However, that progress can't simply continue, it needs to accelerate. 'For China to accomplish its carbon neutrality goal by 2060, it would have to increase solar capacity by ten-fold and wind capacity by seven-fold,' he notes. And that's a problem now, as China is hit by an energy crunch that's caused rolling blackouts at factories. Whether the government decides to remove caps on coal to keep energy flowing remains to be seen.

For that tripling in growth to happen, renewables can't simply be limited to China, the US or the EU, as important as it is for those regions to shift to clean energy. 'We have incredible potential in all parts of the world for wind and solar PV,' adds Bahar. 'There needs to be a big scale-up not only in these advanced markets, but elsewhere. There's huge potential between Africa solar PV and the need for clean energy. The Netherlands makes more solar than the whole of Africa. We need to tap those resources in Africa, Southeast Asia, in Latin America and so on.'

Beyond wind and solar, other renewables such as geothermal, biomass, concentrating solar thermal power and marine projects aren't growing as quickly. 'With solar, costs declined so rapidly over the last few years, but for others, the technologies have higher costs in general,' says Bahar. That's a problem, as such generation sources could be required to help balance the intermittency of solar and wind – and without their further development we may continue to rely on gas or other fossil fuels. To avoid that, governments should take on some of the development risk of such projects.

How can we speed this transition along? The easier to overcome, but by no means trivial, challenges are in engineering and construction – building an undersea HVDC cable or offshore floating wind farm naturally takes time, though we can help companies by sorting out red tape and regulatory approval. Another hurdle is finance and costs, both of which can be mitigated through government incentives where possible, though money will also have to be found to smooth the risks and damages of this massive change, including job losses.

And then there's the politics of it all. We can push governments to reduce approval times and offer public funds to accelerate this transition, but that is likely to temporarily increase energy prices, something no democratically elected politician is eager to do. These efforts can also be counteracted and slowed by incumbents such as fossil-fuel companies and utilities concerned about sunk costs and stranded assets – installing an oil pipeline or running natural gas lines to houses takes time to pay off, and if fossil-fuel use fades before return on investment is achieved, it could leave companies out of pocket.

Hitting net zero by 2050 doesn't give us time to dally, so we need to find ways around such challenges.

Construction

Construction is one challenge to increasing the use of green energies. Permits, public consultations and regulatory approval can take years, regardless of the project type, and that's followed by design and building. For a hydroelectric dam, for example, the whole process can take several years, if not much longer. The Three Gorges Dam was a seventeen-year-long project, Itaipu took a year longer, and the Grand Ethiopian Renaissance Dam required nine years of construction before filling the reservoir could begin, a stage that will take several more years. Construction on Chile's Cerro Dominador solar thermal plant began in 2014 and it opened seven years later. The Dogger Bank offshore wind farm in the North Sea was discussed as far back as 2008 and is not expected to be fully complete by 2026 – and that's if everything goes to plan. These are big projects that take immense time and effort.

That means that any immediate decarbonisation goals – such as net zero reduction plans for 2025 or 2030 – will need to largely be achieved by projects already being built, as well as reductions in energy use, and a massive ramp-up in smaller, faster-to-build projects that rely on new technologies. The key to spurring renewables is to drive down costs of technology and installation, argues McBride from the Breakthrough Institute. 'There's a bunch of things that governments can do to try to speed up that cost decline, such as investing in R&D [research and development] and deployment of early stage technologies,' he says.

Cutting red tape can help. Inna Braverman from Eco Wave Power says it's actually become harder to build wave projects, after governments were burned by early enthusiasm for technologies that eventually failed. 'In the past, many governments set up very supportive legislation for wave energy,' Braverman says. 'But with no companies getting close to actually using the subsidies or support, many of them just cancelled it. Now we're coming into countries asking about licences, and they don't know what's needed. The lack of legislation, policies and regulatory framework makes it hard and it takes longer to get licences to construct.'

Supply chains also take time to get up and running. While demand means manufacturing will respond – which has helped reduce the cost of solar panels – that takes time if left to happen organically, says Wang. At the same time, we need to be wary of costs going up, in particular around critical materials like rare-earth elements for batteries or magnets in wind turbines, adds Wang. 'As renewables get cheaper, the cost of commodities becomes an increasing proportion of the cost of these clean energy technologies,' he says. 'Ensuring that we avoid potential bottlenecks and supply shortages is crucial, because that could slow down our deployment rate.'

Costs

One of the reasons coal is dying off, notes Leo Roberts, research manager at think tank E3G, is the high cost of not just building but running such plants. Coal plants are inefficient at making energy versus other types of production technologies. Alongside the costs of mining, transport and running a complicated plant, coal is inherently expensive – and that's before carbon pricing, pollution scrubbers or other costs are considered.

Paired with the falling rates of solar and wind power, coal can't compete in terms of raw capitalism. 'It's 77 per cent cheaper to build a new wind farm or solar plant than it is to keep an existing coal power station running, let alone build a new one,' Roberts says, explaining that's based on the cost per unit of electricity. That's expected to shift to 95 per cent cheaper in the next three years. 'With every passing day, coal becomes more expensive relatively, and makes less and less sense.'

How much does money matter? One of the reasons why 2019 and 2020 have seen such exceptional growth in wind capacity – more than double – is down to China. According to Bahar, local subsidies were set to end at the end of 2020, so Chinese companies raced to complete projects.

Money talks, and that gives us another set of tools to speed up the shift to renewable energy. Carbon taxes – when the government charges companies or even individuals for each tonne of carbon emitted – can artificially raise the price of fossil fuels, as can requiring emissions filters on plants. On the other hand, subsidies can artificially lower costs for renewables, either at the point of installation or for end-user energy prices. All of these options should be seriously considered if we are to speed up the adoption of sustainable energies.

Financing the future

Remember China's pledge to not fund another international coal plant? Now we need China, and countries like it, to take the money they would have used to support coal plants and instead fund renewable energy plants. 'There's a huge opportunity for the world's financial institutions, for China and other countries in the global north, and for public development banks, to plug this finance gap on renewable energy,' says E3G's

Roberts. 'And this isn't just altruism – investing in renewable energy around the world will pay you back in a way that investing in coal wouldn't. There's money to be made as well.'

Building renewable capacity is faster when cash is flowing – but not enough is. Indeed, $100 billion of annual investment pledged by developed countries to spur on such projects in developing countries still hasn't materialised. The IEA notes that though clean energy projects are increasingly cost-competitive, investments aren't matching what's required to meet sustainability goals.[2]

At the same time, a report led by the Rainforest Action Network (RAN) reveals that the world's sixty biggest banks, including JPMorgan Chase and Citi, have financed fossil fuels and related projects worth $3.8 trillion in the five years following the Paris Agreement, handing billions to companies such as ExxonMobil and Royal Dutch Shell to continue with oil and gas extraction. Compare such figures to the investment in renewable energy, which accounting firm EY says grew 2 per cent to $303.5 billion last year. While that was the second-highest year ever, the company estimates the funding gap to be in the trillions of dollars, with $5.2 trillion required. If banks even reduced some of their funding of fossil-fuel companies, they could go a long way to making up the difference.

But despite the action demanded by the Paris Agreement, the financing handed to fossil-fuel firms was higher in 2020 than in 2016, with much of it led by American banks that have goals to decarbonise their investments by 2050. 'This report separates words from actions, and the picture it paints is alarming: major banks around the world, led by US banks in particular, are fueling climate chaos by dumping trillions of dollars into the fossil fuels that are causing the crisis,' said Ben Cushing, financial advocacy campaign manager for the Sierra Club. 'Big banks don't deserve a pat on the back if their 2050 pledges are not paired with meaningful 2021 actions to cut fossil financing.'[3]

Politics and lobbying

And then there's access and lobbying. While fossil-fuel companies heavily promote their forays into green energy, they invest in campaign groups that do all they can to slow such progress. One report in *The Guardian* points to Shell releasing two reports on the same day.[4] The first was the oil company's annual sustainability report, in which it lists efforts to encourage biofuels, install electric-car charging points, and spur development of green hydrogen.[5] All of these are moves to be welcomed, but on the same day a second report, Shell's Industry Associations Climate Review, revealed payments to a variety of industry associations and lobby groups.[6] It's no surprise that an organisation such as Shell has a wide range of industry memberships, but at the very top of the list in terms of payments was the American Petroleum Institute (API).

What is the API? It's a lobby group representing the fossil-fuel industry, which has spoken out against the very electric cars that Shell is building charging points to support, has been accused of disinformation in a lawsuit brought by the state of Minnesota, and is working to hold back progress away from oil and gas. Indeed, a US senator, Sheldon Whitehouse, said the organisation is being used to redirect ire away from fossil-fuel companies now that it's no longer deemed 'socially acceptable' to deny climate change.[7]

Such activities aren't new. A report in 2019 showed the top five non-state-owned oil and gas companies – BP, Shell, ExxonMobil, Chevron and Total – were spending between them more than $200 million a year to fund lobby groups to slow down climate-focused policies. Fossil-fuel firms clearly believe such lobbying has a positive impact on their businesses, or they wouldn't spend millions on it.

The COP conferences bring countries together in a host nation to discuss plans to mitigate climate change. But even these UN-run confabs can be heavily impacted by corporate sponsorship and government preferences.

COP24, held in Poland, had a pavilion full of coal and opened with a speech from then President Andrzej Duda claiming the fossil fuel didn't 'contradict the protection of the climate and the progress of climate protection'.[8]

COP26, held in the UK, required sponsors to be 'making real contributions to the fight against climate change', though government representatives met with BP to discuss the oil and gas company becoming a key sponsor. Leaked documents seen by Greenpeace from the meetings showed the need to transition away from fossil fuels was discussed, but so too was the need to 'fully recognise the continuing importance of oil and gas in the global economy'.[9] In the end, BP did not end up sponsoring the event.

Besides corporate sponsorship, another problem faced by these climate conferences is that not all fossil-fuel producers are companies – some are nations. The economies of some of the most powerful countries in the world are funded by fossil fuels – and that means they're also dragging their feet. 'There's absolutely a number of countries that are much more reticent to take on such policies,' says Antony Froggatt, deputy director of political analyst Chatham House, pointing to Saudi Arabia and Russia.

In the face of these corporate behemoths and oil-rich nations, does political activism work? E3G's Leo Roberts believes that we have to apply pressure, or at least try. With coal, there are two ways of looking at projects: the gigawatts of energy created by burning coal (and the ensuing emissions), or the number of countries that have sworn off the stuff. For every coal plant that isn't built, that saves tonnes of carbon dioxide. But for every country that pledges to stop using coal or refrain from building new coal plants, there's more pressure on those that still do. 'You need these political signals,' he says. 'The number of countries committing to no new coal ... is a clear signal to the world of the direction that things are moving in ... that keeps the pressure on the countries still building coal plants.' In addition, those countries and companies that do leap ahead will have benefits, as they'll not only own or better understand the technologies involved with the energy transition, but they'll have a sneak peek at the future of the entire system. 'I think that gives them a strategic advantage on a global level,' Roberts says.

All talk?

Cutting red tape and incentivising clean power through discounts and carbon taxes. Investing in renewables rather than fossil fuels. And governments refusing to listen to oil and gas incumbents when it comes to making policy. Each of these measures could help accelerate the future of energy, and there are plenty more ideas to consider.

Yet the main tactic for spurring the shift to renewables isn't always specific actions such as these, but signing accords such as the Paris Agreement, in which signatory countries pledged to work to keep global warming to 1.5 degrees Celsius above pre-industrial levels by reaching net zero by 2050. However, such agreements can be more about talk than action – or, as activist Greta Thunberg said in a speech at a UN youth climate summit: 'Build back better. Blah, blah, blah. Green economy. Blah, blah, blah. Net zero by 2050. Blah, blah, blah ... This is all we hear from our so-called leaders. Words that sound great but so far have not led to action. Our hopes and ambitions drown in their empty promises.'

And she's not wrong. A report from Climate Action Tracker revealed that of all the major countries to sign the 2015 agreement, none are on track with the necessary carbon cuts, though small, less well-developed countries are.[10]

The 2021 edition of the UN Conference of Parties Climate Change Conference, better known as COP26, was held in Glasgow, Scotland. Its goal was to come up with ways to deliver existing 2030 emissions reductions targets, aiming to get countries to agree to a series of actions, some of which directly impact energy. These include accelerating the phasing out of coal, switching to electric vehicles and encouraging investment in renewables – in particular actually delivering that aforementioned $100 billion in finance per year.

Looking just at the host country as an example, it seems unlikely real progress will be made with pledges and promises. After all, the UK is currently powering up coal power plants to make up for gaps in electricity production and investing in opening a new mine to sell coal overseas, in particular to Turkey. So much for phasing out coal, then.

Switching to electric vehicles is another stalled target for the COP26 hosts. The current Conservative government ditched financial incentives to cut prices of electric cars, and though it has a plan to boost the number of charging points, it's largely left that in the hands of oil and gas incumbents such as BP and Shell. And what of encouraging investment in renewables? The UK has set aside £4 billion for hydrogen development, but the vast majority will be spent on blue hydrogen rather than its green, more eco-friendly counterpart.

It's easy to kick the transition to renewable energy into the long grass with net zero deadlines so far out. But we don't have the time for that. Renewable projects take decades to build. We can accelerate the shift to clean energy by cutting red tape and supporting construction projects with regulatory frameworks, by counting the cost of fossil fuels with carbon taxes and subsidising green alternatives, and by coughing up the cash to pay for it all. But without real, practical action, none of this change will happen quickly enough to limit the worst impacts of the climate crisis.

But we know what to do – and if we do get it right, the future of energy is bright with potential. Wind turbines and solar power will offer cheap and clean energy, balanced by hydro, biomass and geothermal. Cars, lorries, ferries and buses will be emissions-free, clearing our streets of deadly air pollution, while alternative fuels will slash the environmental costs of shipping and aviation. Ditching gas and biomass in homes for heating and cooking will save emissions, costs and, in developing countries, lives. Smart, interconnected and microgrids will add resiliency to electricity and make sharing it easier, boosting the economy and reworking geopolitics. This is a future worth building.

Acknowledgements

The climate change crisis doesn't make for cheerful reading, but it has been cheering to speak to a small selection of the many people working to clean up the world's energy. The future of energy is difficult to build, and we all owe thanks to the academics and innovators spending their lives improving such systems, but mine in particular go to everyone who took time out of their own research and product development to speak to me and help inform this book.

Throughout my career, I've been amazed and grateful at the willingness of academics and industry experts to speak to journalists. Thank you to the following for being so generous with your time and patient with my questions: Christine Shearer, programme director for coal at analyst firm Global Energy Monitor; Seaver Wang, climate and energy analyst at the Breakthrough

Institute; Leo Roberts, research manager at think tank E3G; Charles Rougé, lecturer in water resilience at the University of Sheffield; Dr Malte Jansen, of the Centre of Environmental Policy at Imperial College London; Jorge Piñero, co-founder and chief marketing officer of Vortex; Jamie Taylor, senior data scientist at Sheffield Solar; Kathy Hannun, founder of Dandelion Energy; Bianca Sassow of SEaB Energy; Inna Braverman, CEO of Israeli startup Eco Wave Power; Rich Helstrom, director of business development at Constructis; Zoisa North-Bond, CEO of Octopus's generation team; A.J. Grosenbaugh, PowerGen commercial development associate; Stephen Crosher, CEO of RheEnergise; Catalina Spataru, course director of the University College London Energy Institute; Peter Lundberg, global product manager at Hitachi ABB Power Grids; Mike Nugent, head of fleet strategy for Hitachi Europe; Matt Finch, policy director at think tank Transport & Environment; Dr Hu Li, associate professor at the University of Leeds; Jessica Folkerts, bio-bean's head of marketing; Charles Haskell, decarbonisation programme manager at Lloyd's Register; Heymi Bahar, senior analyst at the IEA; Jameson McBride at the Breakthrough Institute; and Antony Froggatt, deputy director of political analyst Chatham House. Apologies to anyone who I may have missed.

I'd also like to acknowledge and thank Our World in Data, whose charts on energy have been invaluable in writing this book, as has research from Carbon Tracker, International Renewable Energy Agency, and the International Energy Agency.

Thanks also to the editorial staff at WIRED and Penguin Random House, in particular Rose Waddilove, Elena Roberts and the proofreaders and editors for making my work so much better – any mistakes are mine, not theirs.

And, as always, thanks to my patient and supportive husband, Michael, who not only helped manage my stress while writing a book during a pandemic while pregnant, but also somehow maintained interest in the many fun facts I ran over to excitedly tell him after every interview or research session. And lastly, thanks to my daughter Eliza for not arriving until after I'd filed my copy. Hopefully some of the solutions presented in this book can help make the world a bit better for her.

Notes

Notes to Introduction   pages 2–3

1   https://ourworldindata.org/emissions-by-sector#energy-
electricity-heat-and-transport-73-2

2   https://www.theguardian.com/science/2021/feb/17/arctic-
heating-winter-storms-climate-change

Notes to 1 The slow death of coal   pages 7–24

1   https://www.theguardian.com/environment/2006/sep/01/
energy.activists

2   https://www.theguardian.com/environment/2006/sep/01/
energy.activists

3   https://www.theguardian.com/environment/2006/sep/01/
energy.activists

4   https://www.theguardian.com/environment/2015/
nov/18/energy-policy-shift-climate-change-amber-rudd-
backburner

5   https://www.theguardian.com/business/2021/sep/13/
     britain-last-coal-power-stations-to-be-paid-huge-sums-
     to-keep-lights-on-record-energy-prices

6   https://numerical.co.in/numerons/collection/
     582ea4c425029d0c1123d15c

7   https://www.eia.gov/todayinenergy/detail.php?id=48696

8   https://www.thedialogue.org/analysis/will-coal-soon-be-
     history-in-latin-america/

9   https://www.ga.gov.au/scientific-topics/energy/resources/
     coal-resources

10   https://ourworldindata.org/electricity-mix

11   https://www.axios.com/natural-gas-branding-battle-
     89eb1de7-79cb-4624-a1c5-cca0a5df2170.html

12   A terawatt-hour is the larger version of what you see on
     your energy bill, which is likely to be a kilowatt-hour.

13   https://ourworldindata.org/energy/country/united-states?
     country=USA~DEU~GBR~CHN

14   https://ourworldindata.org/energy/country/china

15   https://www.bloombergquint.com/business/china-s-
     economic-planning-body-says-coal-prices-could-fall-more

16   https://www.irena.org/newsroom/pressreleases/2020/
     Jun/Renewables-Increasingly-Beat-Even-Cheapest-Coal-
     Competitors-on-Cost

17   https://carbontracker.org/coal-developers-risk-600-
     billion-as-renewables-outcompete-worldwide/

18   https://www.un.org/sg/en/content/secretary-generals-
     statement-the-ipcc-working-group-1-report-the-physical-
     science-basis-of-the-sixth-assessment

19   https://ourworldindata.org/electricity-mix

20   https://www.theguardian.com/business/2021/sep/13/
     britain-last-coal-power-stations-to-be-paid-huge-sums-
     to-keep-lights-on-record-energy-prices

Notes to 2 The big players   pages 32–64

1   https://www.alberta.ca/keystone-xl-pipeline-project.
     aspx

2   https://ourworldindata.org/electricity-mix#fossil-fuels-
     what-share-of-electricity-comes-from-fossil-fuels

3   https://www.hydropower.org/iha/discover-history-of-
     hydropower

4   https://www.renewableenergyworld.com/baseload/
    hydroelectric-plants-have-fastest-start-up-time-of-u-s-
    electric-generators/#gref

5   https://www.bbc.co.uk/news/science-environment-46098118

6   https://www.theguardian.com/cities/2019/sep/12/they-
    are-barbaric-turkey-prepares-to-flood-12000-year-old-
    city-to-build-dam

7   https://archive.internationalrivers.org/campaigns/three-
    gorges-dam

8   https://thenarwhal.ca/mercury-rising-muskrat-falls-dam-
    threatens-inuit-way-of-life/

9   https://theconversation.com/energy-sector-is-one-of-the-
    largest-consumers-of-water-in-a-drought-threatened-
    world-59109

10 https://www.wwdmag.com/one-water/california-shuts-down-
    major-hydroelectric-plant-due-low-water-levels-lake-oroville

11 https://www.power-technology.com/features/drought-
    limit-hydropowers-role-energy-mix/

12 https://www.theguardian.com/world/2017/dec/08/malawi-
    blackouts-drought-hydro-power

13 https://www.theguardian.com/world/2015/jan/23/brazil-worst-drought-history

14 https://www.aljazeera.com/gallery/2021/8/30/drying-euphrates-syria-disaster

15 https://www.wired.co.uk/article/hydropower-amazon

16 https://qz.com/2038475/managing-chinas-dams-is-trickier-in-era-of-climate-change/

17 https://news.sky.com/story/uttarakhand-dam-disaster-what-caused-indias-deadly-flood-12214731

18 https://www.latimes.com/world-nation/story/2020-07-20/china-blasts-dam-to-release-floodwaters-as-death-toll-rises

19 https://www.sserenewables.com/offshore-wind/projects/dogger-bank/

20 https://www.theguardian.com/business/2021/jan/02/dogger-banks-giant-turbines-herald-a-wind-of-change-in-uk-industry

21 https://www.axpo.com/ch/en/about-us/magazine.detail.html/magazine/renewable-energy/power-from-the-mountains-extern.html

22 https://ourworldindata.org/electricity-mix#wind-what-share-of-electricity-comes-from-wind

23   https://www.theguardian.com/environment/2015/jul/10/
      denmark-wind-windfarm-power-exceed-electricity-
      demand

24   http://eprints.lse.ac.uk/58422/1/_lse.ac.uk_storage_
      LIBRARY_Secondary_libfile_shared_repository_Content_
      SERC%20discussion%20papers_2014_sercdp0159.pdf

25   https://www.wired.co.uk/article/china-wind-farms-
      climate-crisis

26   https://theconversation.com/robin-hushed-wind-turbines-
      are-making-songbirds-change-their-tune-109136

27   https://theconversation.com/wind-turbines-arent-
      quite-apex-predators-but-the-truth-is-far-more-
      interesting-106480

28   https://abcbirds.org/blog21/wind-turbine-mortality/

29   https://onlinelibrary.wiley.com/doi/full/10.1002/
      ece3.6592

30   https://www.wired.co.uk/bc/article/innovating-towards-a-
      new-era-of-sustainable-energy

31   https://www.energy.gov/eere/articles/wind-turbines-
      bigger-better

32   https://theconversation.com/floating-wind-farms-how-to-make-them-the-future-of-green-electricity-142847

33   https://www.edp.com/en/innovation/windfloat

34   https://www.equinor.com/en/what-we-do/floating-wind.html

35   https://newatlas.com/energy/worlds-biggest-wind-turbine-mingyang/

36   https://challenergy.com/en-news/_october_12020_we_have_updated_the_maximum_recorded_instantaneous-2/

37   https://www.zmescience.com/ecology/green-living/worlds-first-airborne-wind-farm-42324/

38   https://www.energy.gov/eere/solar/how-does-solar-work

39   https://www.iea.org/reports/world-energy-outlook-2020

40   https://www.nasa.gov/ames/arads

41   https://www.google.co.uk/maps/place/Cerro+Dominador+-+Complejo+Solar/@-22.7717413,-69.4821745,1185m/data=!3m1!1e3!4m5!3m4!1s0x96ac2801b319c631:0x7cb9e03f0b3de17c!8m2!3d-22.770895!4d-69.4791183

42   https://www.pv-magazine.com/2020/04/21/italy-deployed-737-mw-of-solar-in-2019/

43 https://www.pv-magazine.com/2020/05/22/italian-homeowners-can-now-install-pv-systems-for-free/

44 https://www.energy.gov/eere/solar/articles/pv-cells-101-primer-solar-photovoltaic-cell

45 https://www.ft.com/content/97e6b15d-4b7d-4578-8d1a-f43df77ff116

46 https://www.ft.com/content/97e6b15d-4b7d-4578-8d1a-f43df77ff116

47 According to the International Renewable Energy Agency (IRENA).

48 https://today.oregonstate.edu/news/installing-solar-panels-agricultural-lands-maximizes-their-efficiency-new-study-shows

49 https://www.wired.co.uk/bc/article/innovating-towards-a-new-era-of-sustainable-energy

50 https://www.wired.co.uk/article/solar-farms

51 https://www.wired.co.uk/article/solar-weather-forecasting

52 https://platiosolar.com/barcelona-installs-spains-first-solar-energy-pavement/

53 https://www.sciencedirect.com/science/article/pii/
S0038092X20311853

54 https://oceansofenergy.blue/2020/12/02/solar-
energy-and-sea-weed-together-at-sea-for-the-first-time/

55 https://www.zdnet.com/article/singapore-opens-floating-
60-megawatt-solar-farm/

56 https://www.sciencedirect.com/science/article/pii/
S0038092X2100116X

57 https://www.science.org/doi/10.1126/science.1155398

Notes to 3 What's next   pages 68–93

1 https://www.eib.org/attachments/pipeline/20080135_nts1_
en.pdf

2 https://www.government.is/topics/business-and-industry/
energy/

3 https://www.iea.org/reports/heat-pumps

4 https://www.clientearth.org/projects/the-greenwashing-
files/drax/

5 https://www.drax.com/wp-content/uploads/2020/03/
Drax_AR2019_Web.pdf

6   https://ember-climate.org/project/the-burning-question/

7   https://zerowasteeurope.eu/2019/11/copenhagen-incineration-plant/

8   https://www.imperial.ac.uk/news/228373/major-nuclear-fusion-milestone-reached-ignition/

Notes to 4 Smart grids   pages 98–117

1   https://www.cnbc.com/2021/02/17/how-the-texas-power-grid-failed-and-what-could-stop-it-from-happening-again.html

2   https://www.buzzfeednews.com/article/peteraldhous/texas-winter-storm-power-outage-death-toll

3   https://www.powergen-renewable-energy.com/wp-content/uploads/2019/11/191103_PowerGen-Series-B-Final.pdf

4   https://openknowledge.worldbank.org/handle/10986/31926

5   https://www.wired.co.uk/article/mini-power-grids

6   https://www.goodnewsnetwork.org/solar-powered-apartment-in-new-orleans-kept-the-lights-on-through-ida/

7   https://www.greenbiz.com/article/7-companies-making-their-mark-commercial-microgrids

8   https://www.wired.co.uk/article/bc/renewable-energy-is-
      helping-the-isles-of-scilly-environment

9   https://www.aer.gov.au/news-release/hornsdale-in-court-
      for-inability-to-provide-contingency-services-as-offered

10   https://e360.yale.edu/features/in-boost-for-renewables-
      grid-scale-battery-storage-is-on-the-rise

11   https://www.energy-storage.news/uks-largest-battery-
      storage-project-at-640mwh-gets-go-ahead-from-
      government/

12   https://www.nationalgrid.com/stories/energy-explained/
      what-are-electricity-interconnectors

13   https://www.themanufacturer.com/articles/china-wants-
      to-build-a-global-power-grid-gei-worth-50tr/

Notes to 5 Electrify everything   pages 122–130

1   https://www.electrive.com/2021/03/02/worlds-largest-
      electric-ferry-yet-goes-into-service-in-norway/

2   https://www.bbc.co.uk/news/business-50233206

3   https://www.intelligenttransport.com/transport-
      news/120053/electric-ferry/

4   https://plugboats.com/bangkok-becoming-electric-ferry-
     capital-of-the-world/

5   https://plugboats.com/worlds-busiest-ferry-systems-
     going-electric-hybrid/

6   https://eandt.theiet.org/content/articles/2020/10/uk-s-
     first-electric-ferry-will-take-to-the-seas-in-2021/

7   https://www.theguardian.com/environment/2019/nov/25/
     are-electric-vehicles-really-so-climate-friendly

8   https://www.theguardian.com/environment/2019/nov/25/
     are-electric-vehicles-really-so-climate-friendly

9   https://uploads.volkswagen-newsroom.com/
     system/production/uploaded_files/14448/file/
     da01b16ac9b580a3c8bc190ea2af27db4e0d4546/
     Klimabilanz_von_E-Fahrzeugen_Life_Cycle_Engineering.
     pdf?1556110703

10   https://www.bloomberg.com/opinion/articles/2021–03-10/
     air-pollution-kills-far-more-people-than-covid-ever-will

11   https://www.theatlantic.com/technology/archive/2018/02/
     city-noise-might-be-making-you-sick/553385/

12   https://www.bmj.com/content/374/bmj.n1954

13   https://www.independent.co.uk/life-style/gadgets-and-
      tech/news/tesla-model-y-s3xy-elon-musk-new-latest-
      features-cost-price-car-a8825141.html

14   https://insideevs.com/news/524575/us-ford-plugin-sales-
      july2021/

15   https://www.cnbc.com/2021/01/08/pickup-trucks-
      dominate-americas-10-best-selling-vehicles-of-2020.
      html

16   https://www.autocar.co.uk/car-news/new-cars/ford-f-150-
      lightning-563bhp-electric-pick-truck-revealed

17   https://www.thedrive.com/news/40840/how-the-ford-f-
      150-lightnings-chief-engineer-linda-zhang-brought-the-
      world-an-electric-pickup

18   https://twitter.com/cspan/status/1394733645903040517

19   https://www.reuters.com/business/autos-transportation/
      exclusive-ford-doubles-lightning-production-target-
      strong-pre-launch-demand-2021-08-23/

20   https://www.canalys.com/newsroom/global-electric-
      vehicle-sales-up-160-in-h1-2021-despite-supply-
      constraints

21 https://theicct.org/blog/staff/china-new-energy-vehicles-jan2021

22 https://www.iea.org/reports/global-ev-outlook-2020

23 https://www.wired.co.uk/article/chinese-electric-car-companies-tesla-byd-jac-motors

24 https://ourworldindata.org/grapher/fossil-fuels-share-energy?tab=chart&country=~CHN

25 https://dataportal.orr.gov.uk/media/1842/rail-infrastructure-assets-2019-20.pdf

Notes to 6 Alternative fuels   pages 134–155

1 https://www.eia.gov/outlooks/ieo/pdf/transportation.pdf

2 https://www.wired.co.uk/article/hydrogen-ships-eu

3 https://www.wired.co.uk/article/hydrogen-ships-eu

4 https://www.atag.org/facts-figures.html

5 https://www.bp.com/en/global/air-bp/news-and-views/views/what-is-sustainable-aviation-fuel-saf-and-why-is-it-important.html

6   https://ihsmarkit.com/research-analysis/sustainable-
    aviation-fuel-market-still-in-infancy-due-to-cost-.html

7   https://www.anthropocenemagazine.org/2021/06/sustainable-
    aviation-fuels-could-be-even-better-than-we-thought

8   https://mediacentre.britishairways.com/news/15092021/
    as-the-uk-prepares-to-host-the-cop26-climate-summit-
    british-airways-and-its-partners-achieve-record-
    carbon-emissions-reductions-as-part-of-their-perfect-
    flight-demonstration-to-show-how-aviation-is-
    decarbonising?ref=News

9   https://theconversation.com/contrails-from-aeroplanes-
    warm-the-planet-heres-how-new-low-soot-fuels-can-
    help-162779

10 https://www.bbc.com/future/article/20201116-climate-
    change-how-to-cut-the-carbon-emissions-from-heating

11 https://www.wired.co.uk/article/hydrogen-ships-eu

12 https://www.irena.org/-/media/Files/IRENA/Agency/
    Publication/2018/Sep/IRENA_Hydrogen_from_renewable_
    power_2018.pdf

13   https://www.forbes.com/sites/rrapier/2020/06/06/
      estimating-the-carbon-footprint-of-hydrogen-
      production/#3866364b24bd

14   https://www.anthropocenemagazine.org/2019/03/simple-
      method-to-produce-clean-hydrogen-fuel-from-seawater/

15   https://onlinelibrary.wiley.com/doi/full/10.1002/ese3.956

16   https://www.theguardian.com/environment/2021/aug/17/
      uk-homes-low-carbon-hydrogen-economy-jobs

17   https://www.spglobal.com/marketintelligence/en/
      news-insights/latest-news-headlines/experts-explain-
      why-green-hydrogen-costs-have-fallen-and-will-keep-
      falling-63037203

18   https://www.reuters.com/article/us-green-hydrogen-s-ipo-
      idUSKCN2DJ19X

19   https://www.maersk.com/news/articles/2020/05/26/
      leading-danish-companies-join-forces-on-an-ambitious-
      sustainable-fuel-project

20   https://theconversation.com/hydrogen-where-is-low-
      carbon-fuel-most-useful-for-decarbonisation-147696

21   https://www.wired.co.uk/article/hydrogen-ships-eu

22 http://alstom.com/press-releases-news/2021/8/
alstoms-coradia-ilint-hydrogen-train-runs-first-time-
sweden

23 https://www.bbc.co.uk/news/business-54242176

24 https://theconversation.com/hydrogen-could-become-the-
new-fuel-for-cooking-heres-how-66241

25 https://www.reuters.com/business/sustainable-business/
maersk-orders-eight-vessels-able-run-carbon-neutral-
methanol-2021-08-24/

26 https://www.dfds.com/en/about/fuels/green-methanol

27 https://www.maersk.com/news/articles/2021/09/08/
maersk-invests-in-wastefuel-to-develop-green-bio-
methanol

28 https://www.ft.com/content/800faea2-1024-4ea6-ade6-
1680820e925b

29 https://www.reuters.com/business/sustainable-business/
maersk-orders-eight-vessels-able-run-carbon-neutral-
methanol-2021-08-24/

30 https://spectrum.ieee.org/why-the-shipping-industry-is-
betting-big-on-ammonia

31   https://arena.gov.au/projects/feasibility-study-for-a-green-hydrogen-and-ammonia-project/

32   https://spectrum.ieee.org/why-the-shipping-industry-is-betting-big-on-ammonia

33   https://www.lr.org/en/latest-news/industry-leaders-join-forces-on-ammonia-fuelled-tanker-project/

34   https://www.wartsila.com/media/news/14-07-2021-wartsila-launches-major-test-programme-towards-carbon-free-solutions-with-hydrogen-and-ammonia-2953362

Notes to 7 Making it happen   pages 158–174

1   https://thebreakthrough.org/issues/energy/narwhal-slope

2   https://www.iea.org/reports/world-energy-investment-2020/energy-financing-and-funding

3   https://www.ran.org/press-releases/bankingonclimatechaos2021/

4   https://www.theguardian.com/environment/2021/jul/19/big-oil-climate-crisis-lobby-group-api

5   https://reports.shell.com/sustainability-report/2020/achieving-net-zero-emissions/fuelling-mobility.html

6   https://www.shell.com/promos/sustainability/
    industry-associations-climate-review-2021/_
    jcr_content.stream/1617784370604/
    bbe8a29c319bef3c08424184b21543dc6c032239/shell-
    industry-associations-report-2021.pdf

7   https://www.theguardian.com/environment/2021/jul/19/
    big-oil-climate-crisis-lobby-group-api

8   https://www.euronews.com/green/2020/08/20/cop26-
    may-refuse-sponsorship-from-big-polluters

9   https://unearthed.greenpeace.org/2020/05/25/cop26-
    minister-bp-key-stakeholder-climate-conference/

10 https://edition.cnn.com/2021/09/15/world/climate-
    pledges-insufficient-cat-intl/index.html

Index